FELICIANA'S
CALIFORNIA
MIRACLE

Tomasa, Feliciana, and Eustaquía

FELICIANA'S CALIFORNIA MIRACLE

Esther J. Comstock

Illustrated by Dave Comstock

Comstock Bonanza Press
Grass Valley, California

© 1985 Esther J. Comstock
Published by Comstock Bonanza Press
18919 William Quirk Memorial Drive
Grass Valley California 95945
Printed in the United States of America

Library of Congress Cataloging in Publication Data

Comstock, Esther J.
Feliciana's California miracle.

Bibliography: p. 173
Includes index.
1. Gutiérrez de Arballo, María Feliciana.
2. Mexicans—California—Biography.
3. Spaniards—California—History—18th century.
4. Anza, Juan Bautista de, 1735-1788.
5. California—Biography.
6. California—History—To 1846.
I. Title
F870.M5A933 1985   979.4'02'0924 [B]   85-9707
ISBN 0-933994-03-6
ISBN 0-933994-04-4 (pbk.)

For all my friends who wanted a "girl's story" next.

". . . it may be doubtful if the pioneer period of any other American State has had a more complete mass of original authoritative data made ready for historian's use."
—Marie Northrup, *Spanish-Mexican Families of Early California, 1769–1850.*

CONTENTS

Maps

ACKNOWLEDGMENTS

I wish to express my great appreciation to Shyrle Hacker for her sensitive help in breathing life into the diaries of Captain Juan Bautista de Anza and the Franciscan Padre Pedro Font—leaders of the 1775 expedition from Sonora, Mexico, to San Gabriel, California—and into the lives of those who accompanied them.

I wish to thank my son, David A. Comstock, for his careful and sympathetic editing, his illustrations, and most of all for his skill as a book designer.

I wish to give thanks to Ardis Comstock, Dave's wife, who often acts as a "gofer" and encourages us both.

I wish to thank my family and friends, who continually encourage me to keep going.

And last, but not least, thanks to my patient husband, who often has to share time with the typewriter for my attention.

GLOSSARY

Abuela	Grandmother.
Adobe	Sun-dried clay brick; brick building.
Aguardiente	Brandy.
Alabado	Hymn of praise.
Bollito	Small cake or roll.
Buenos días	Good day; good morning.
Buenas noches	Good night.
Cañon	Deep gorge or ravine; storm drain.
Capitán	Captain.
Comandante	Commandant; commander.
Corral	Fenced yard for animals.
Día	Day.
Dios	God.
Don; Doña	Master; Mistress (used with first name).
Dulce	Sweet; candy or dried fruit.
El	The.
Es nada	It is nothing; not important.
Fandango	Lively Spanish dance.
Fiesta	Feast; festival.
Gracias	Thanks; thank you.
Madre; Mamá	Mother; Mamma.
Mamacita	Mother.
Mañana	Tomorrow.
Mantilla	Woman's head covering.
Medano	Sand dune.
Mes	Month.
Mestizo	Mixed ancestry; Indian and Spanish.
Mezquite	Spiny shrub of the pea family.
Mi; mía, mis	My or mine.
Mi casa es su casa	My house is yours.
Muchas	Many; a lot.
Nada	Nothing.
Niña	Girl.
Niñita	Little girl.
Noche	Night.

Ojos	Eyes.
Padre; papá	Father; papa.
Panocha	Brown sugar candy.
Pinole	Corn or mezquite beans ground into meal.
Plaza	Town square; market-place.
Poncho	Cloak.
Posada	Inn; traditional Christmas pageant.
Presidio	Garrison; military fort.
Pueblo	Town; village.
Querida	Beloved; darling.
Rancho	Stock farm; huts where herders live.
Rebozo	Long scarf worn on head by women.
Rey	King.
Sargente	Sergeant.
Señor	Master; Sir; Mr.
Señora	Mistress; Lady; Mrs. (used with last name).
Serape	Shawl; blanket-like covering.
Sí	Yes.
Tortilla	Flat cornmeal pancake.
Trovador	Troubadour; poet.
Tus ojos	Your eyes.
Uno	One.
Vaya con Dios	Go with God; God be with you.
Viva!	Long live! Hurrah!

FOREWORD

This is the story of *Señora* María Feliciana Gutiérrez de Arballo, who came to California with Anza in 1775 with her two little girls. She was the young widow who was the talk of the expedition, and was referred to by both Anza and *Padre* Font in their diaries.

This, the first of the great exodus heading for California, did not depart from Independence, Missouri, which perhaps explains why it is never described in United States history books. Instead, it left from the Mexican states of Sinaloa and Sonora. The 240 colonists, including more than 100 children, were to found a new *pueblo* alongside San Francisco Bay. The expedition was led by Captain Juan Bautista de Anza, his able lieutenant, José Joaquín Moraga, and three Franciscan *padres*.

From the viewpoint of U.S. history books, it had two strikes against it. First, it was composed entirely of Spanish-Mexicans, and second, it was the only such expedition made entirely overland from Mexico. *Padre* Junípero Serra, Gaspar de Portolá, and Fernando Rivera y Moncado went from Mexico to Baja California by ship in 1769, and then traveled overland to San Diego. They brought no settlers.

Unlike the massive and disorganized wagon trains of the nineteenth century, this trip was planned meticulously from start to finish: route, food, clothing, animals, and welfare of the colonists after they reached the destination.

Anza had dreamed of such a trip for years. He talked with Bucareli, the Viceroy of Mexico, who gave him permission to take a small force and explore the area to the Pacific in 1774. Anza crossed the deserts and marked watering holes. He found a pass over the southern Sierra and continued to the mission at Monterey. On the return trip he found shortcuts and was able to eliminate 200 miles from the journey.

Bucareli then dealt with King Carlos III of Spain. Anza had told the viceroy of the poverty of people in the Sinaloa region of Mexico, where the once busy silver mines now were closed. Bucareli informed the king that people would need clothing (from head to toe), food, saddle animals, gifts for the Indians, and support in the new location.

Spain was aware of the trade in the Pacific among the English, Dutch, Russian, and Yankee galleons. King Carlos knew they needed more than small missions to maintain their fragile hold on New Spain. He agreed to send all that Anza had asked for.

To quote Frank Riley in *De Anza's Trail Today:*

Anza went across the desert, over the Sierras and on to the Mission at Monterey, a feat comparable to what Lewis and Clark accomplished thirty years later. Lewis and Clark got all the ink in the history books, but if they had then returned to Missouri and made a second trip with 240 colonists in tow, their place in history would have been more comparable to Anza's— providing they had been able to lead their settlers through the worst storm recorded in the southern Sierras, and with the loss of only one life, a young mother in childbirth.

Unfortunately, in San Gabriel Anza met California's Captain Commander, *Don* Fernando Xavier de Rivera y Moncada, who did his best to sabotage the expedition. He forbade Anza taking the colonists to San Francisco Bay. Anza by-passed him—after all, his orders were from the viceroy—and with Moraga went on to Monterey. Here he waited for Rivera's permission. It never came. Anza was ordered back to Mexico.

Anza, Moraga and a few soldiers explored the proposed site for the future *pueblo* and found it acceptable, which Rivera had said it was not. Anza left Moraga in charge and returned as ordered. Lieutenant Moraga, with the blessings of the Monterey mission *padres*, fulfilled the commission from the viceroy, taking the colonists to the shores of San Francisco Bay. Only then did Rivera send his permission.

Anza returned to the Colorado River and took Chief Palma with him to Mexico City as he had promised. Anza never set foot in California again. He became governor of New Mexico, Mexico, where he made peace with the Indian tribes.

Later Rivera went with a large force to the Colorado crossing controlled by the Yumas and their chief Palma. Whereas Anza had treated these tribes with respect, later soldiers had too often abused the natives. When Rivera arrived, with his haughty disdain for the Indians, the Yumas revolted. In a wild slaughter that Chief Palma could not control, the Indians killed Rivera, his troops, some white settlers in a nearby *pueblo*, and even the beloved *Padre* Francisco Garcés, who had roamed the west alone and unafraid.

There were no more mass crossings of the Colorado until General Kearny's troops came through in the 1840s.

This book is based on the diaries of Anza and Font as given in Herbert E. Bolton's *Anza's California Expeditions: History of Early California*, Volumes 1 and 3. As this is an historical novel, I have taken some liberties, but all persons mentioned as members of the expedition are listed by Zoeth S. Eldredge in *The Beginnings of San Francisco*, Volume 1.

All Indian names and those of non-members of Anza's group are fictitious, as is the story of the turquoise charm, although blue stones were highly regarded by Indians of many tribes.

There were three bachelor soldiers listed in the party, and from their number I arbitrarily chose *Don* Francisco Muños, as there are no records to show what happened to him later.

Other than the celebration of the *Posada* on Christmas Eve, all events en route are mentioned by either Anza or Font or both in the diaries.

E.J.C.

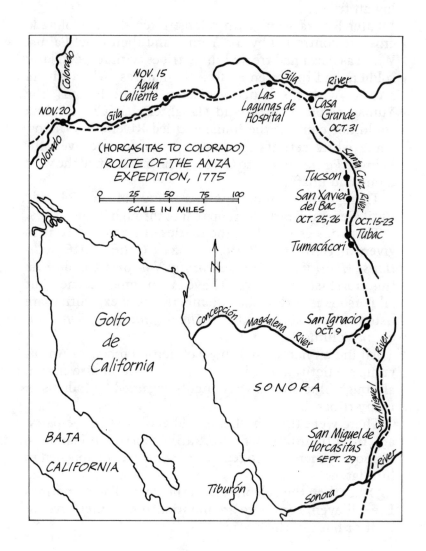

NOV. 15
Agua
Caliente

NOV. 20

Colorado

Gila

Colorado

Gila River

Las
Lagunas de
Hospital

Casa
Grande
OCT. 31

Santa Cruz River

(HORCASITAS TO COLORADO)
ROUTE OF THE ANZA
EXPEDITION, 1775

0   25   50   75   100
SCALE IN MILES

N

Tucson

San Xavier
del Bac
OCT. 25, 26

OCT. 15-23
Túbac

Tumacácori

Golfo
de
California

Concepción

Magdalena River

San Ignacio
OCT. 9

River

SONORA

San Miguel

BAJA

CALIFORNIA

Tiburón

San Miguel de
Horcasitas
SEPT. 29

River

Sonora

xiv

HORCASITAS TO TUBAC

The Journey Begins

CHAPTER 1

Feliciana Gutiérrez de Arballo stood in the center of the white-walled, dirt-floored room of the little *adobe* house. The young widow stared in disbelief as the soldiers finished unloading from their cart a pile of blankets, yards and yards of white *pueblo* cotton and linen for jackets and skirts. Small piles consisted of shoes, stockings and yards of yellow ribbon.

Her two little girls pressed back against the wall, wide-eyed with curiosity.

"Is all of this for us, *Mamá*?" asked six-year-old Tomasa.

"For us, *Mamá*?" echoed four-year-old Eustaquía.

"*Sí, mis niñitas*, for us," answered Feliciana, not knowing whether to laugh or cry. In this *mañana* land one didn't believe promises until they came to pass. As she tried to decide what next to do, a voice called out from the doorway.

"What's going on? Are these the things *Capitán* Anza promised you? Whatever will you do with it all, Feliciana?" It was her friend Lupe, the one friend she would miss more than all the others.

"I've been watching them unload and dying to come in. Oh, Feliciana, I hoped this day would never come. Sometimes I wished we had said we would go with you to California. But when your José died, I was sure you would change your mind and stay," and Lupe burst into tears.

"Oh, Lupe, don't cry or I'll start too," said Feliciana, hugging Lupe close. "Come, help me sort these things. My brother will be here shortly. You know him, he'll be angry if I'm not ready."

She wished the soldiers had come sooner. Yesterday she

had arranged her few household goods ready to be moved to her mother's home in nearby Horcasitas. Carlos, her brother, had said he would be by with the cart today. He would grumble if she wasn't ready. He always grumbled when things didn't suit him.

Lupe wiped her eyes and tried to smile. "Of course I'll help you. But where do we start?"

The young women looked around the room, speculating. In their early twenties, they were simply dressed in the white cotton blouses and dark skirts, typical of this warm dusty region. The abundance displayed overwhelmed Feliciana, for no soldier's pay could ever purchase what Anza had sent.

Lupe picked up one of the blankets. "Good heavens, these blankets!" she exclaimed. "Whenever will you need these? All right, all right, I remember Anza said it would be cold on the trip. And this lovely cotton," Lupe touched it gently. "Surely this will last you for many years. Where will you be when you are using it? Oh, Fel, how can you go so far? I'll never see you again," and she started to cry.

Feliciana was distressed, too. She looked at the yards of white cotton, knowing she must find time to make some into petticoats and chemises for herself. The rest would be used for the girls as they needed new clothes.

Lupe felt of the heavy serge and linen, and Feliciana knew that Lupe had never had such materials for herself, either.

"I'll have my mother's sewing girl help me make that into skirts and jackets," Feliciana said. "It is hard to think, though, that there will be a need for such heavy clothes. I wonder how it will feel to be cold enough to want them? Perhaps the *capitán* exaggerated."

With Lupe's help and some from the little girls, Feliciana had the piles rearranged to her satisfaction.

Carlos arrived shortly after, surprised (Feliciana chuckled to herself) to see everything in order. He was a tall, well-built young man, but with a sour expression as though he expected nothing good of life. He expertly surveyed the goods waiting transportation before loading them into the cart.

As he placed the heavy blankets in the bottom, he ex-

4

claimed, "Whenever will you need these? Foolish waste of money!" Then followed the few household articles that must be stored at her mother's house.

Grumbling constantly, he loaded the small chests filled with Feliciana's treasures, too special to be left behind.

Feliciana had agonized over which clothes to pack. Her wedding dress would go, of course, for perhaps someday Tomasa would wear it. Twice she set aside the yellow ruffled one. She loved it, but when and where would it be appropriate? In the end she packed it along with the elegant *mantilla* and comb her mother had passed on to her. Maybe, in that dim, far-off place called California, she would give them to Eustaquía.

A sudden panic seized her as Carlos put the children's clothes chests and her pots and cooking utensils into the cart. These and her two beautiful little girls would be the only reminders of the happy life she and her young soldier husband, José Gutiérrez, had shared.

How were they to live in the new land with only clothes and a few pans? Then she saw Carlos tying the firmly woven *rebozos* on top. These held the stockings, ribbons and other gifts from Anza. The panic left her for she knew she would never go back on her word that she would continue the trip even without José.

Carlos, again reminding his sister of the trouble she was causing her family, climbed onto the cart and drove off.

Feliciana turned and gazed wistfully at what had been her home. She said a silent farewell to the little one room *adobe* now awaiting a new family.

She turned to meet the others of her neighbors who had come to say their goodbyes and wish her well. There was much weeping and embracing.

"How can you think of going so far?" asked Ana, a tired-looking older woman. Feliciana knew that Ana had eleven children and silently agreed she herself would not be going under such conditions.

"It sounds exciting," exclaimed a bubbly young woman. "But think of the Indians—" and her voice trailed off.

"Feliciana, I wish you well, but after all, land is land. How do you know California will be any different? At least here we manage to grow enough to eat."

"We'll miss you, Feliciana. Your singing and dancing helped make life here more bearable." This was Marina, another dear friend. "I hope you do find a better life ahead."

Feliciana was touched. She knew all their husbands had been approached by Anza but had turned him down. Their wives were concerned about her future. Her tears mingled with theirs. With a heavy heart she knew they would probably never see each other again.

Feliciana untied Gallardo, José's chestnut horse. When his master had died, killed by Apache Indians, he had been given to Feliciana. He nickered happily as she put Tomasa on his back. He was used to the girls and their mother riding him now.

Lupe and Feliciana held each other in a last embrace, tears streaming down their cheeks. Eustaquía, tugging at her skirt, reminded her mother it was time to go.

Feliciana wiped away her tears and smoothed back the errant curls from her face into the thick braid in back. She hoped she looked presentable as she started the ride back to her mother's home.

Just as she took her seat in the side-saddle and Lupe had picked up Eustaquía, Feliciana heard the anxious voice calling, "Wait for me!"

The other women drew aside as a small, crippled brown nut of a woman struggled between them. It was Juana, the *mestizo* woman who lived alone, ignored by these pure-blooded Spanish women. Feliciana had often wondered how she survived on the small garden she tended. Sometimes Feliciana had taken leftovers to her.

Juana pushed close to Feliciana, pulling a leather thong from around her neck.

"If I were your age, Feliciana, I would go with you. Since I can't, I want you to have this good luck charm of mine."

Feliciana heard the amused murmur of the women—a good luck charm? What good luck had Juana ever known? She silently argued with them: she is giving me something special of hers and I shall certainly need all the good luck I can get.

The old woman put the greasy worn thong in Feliciana's

hand. From the strip hung a bright greenish-blue stone, the color of the sky in the early morning.

"This is for you to wear," continued the dry old voice. "But your best good luck charms are your girls. Tomasa will be a comfort in years to come. Your little one," the gnarled old hand patted the curly head, "will bring you fame and much family in the new land.

"*Vaya con Dios*, Feliciana. I will miss you and pray each day for you."

Before Feliciana could speak and thank her, she had turned and hobbled back through the quieted neighbors. The thong *was* greasy, but Feliciana slipped the gift over her head, and called to the disappearing old woman.

"*Muchas gracias*, Juana. I shall wear it always."

Lupe handed up Eustaquía. Then, tearfully, they all waved goodbye as Felicia turned Gallardo down the road to Horcasitas, the first step on that long journey to the unknown land called California.

CHAPTER 2

Feliciana let the horse set his own pace, for she was in no hurry. The tears continued as she thought of the days ahead with no José. He had been killed several months ago, just after they had signed with *Capitán* Juan Bautista de Anza for the expedition to California.

She rationalized that this journey would help her overcome her grief. This was a second wrench—the breaking with all of her past life. How would she live in a new place with no man to help her? Just maybe someone new would come into her life. It was a tantalizing thought, but she guiltily pushed it aside. She wiped away her tears. This was no time for dreaming. Her most pressing problem for now was her mother.

She dreaded the time until the expedition would leave. Since José's death, her family had argued and tried to dissuade her from going ahead with her plans to travel with Anza. Their constant complaints went round and round in her head.

"No proper woman with small children would dream of going on such a hazardous expedition." "You are too young to travel unchaperoned." "Anza had no business encouraging you to continue. He must be a man of low morals."

The more they argued, the more set Feliciana became. If she stayed home, she would be subject to her father's authority until she married again. She had no desire to marry at present, nor did she want her father to choose a new husband, either. Her married life was now ended and she must set her mind to the new life ahead.

It seemed ages ago that she and José had signed with Anza for his expedition to the New Spain. They saw little future but Indian-fighting in this once wealthy mining area, but now only a poor section of Sonora, Mexico. They had speculated long and often about what the new land called California would be like.

They were young, in love and wanted something better for their two girls and the more babies Feliciana hoped to have. The mines in Sonora had run out, farming was poor and soldiering was little better. The promise of animals, fertile new land and equipment to each soldier at the end of a ten-year stint was enticing.

Feliciana remembered few of the details: only that they would be able to grow everything, and that there were many trees and lush green meadows. They had passed over his warnings that it would be a hard trip through Apache lands, across deserts and over steep mountains. Nothing in her background helped Feliciana understand the actual hazards of the trip, though.

Now Feliciana rode alone, steeling herself to the arguments she would face at her mother's. When they arrived, the children were engulfed in her mother's arms.

"My poor little ones," cried *Señora* Arballo, tears streaming down her face. "You are here at last. Come, come," she called to the maid nearby, "take them to their rooms."

Feliciana stood in the bedroom that had once been hers. Here she had been a young girl, carefree and surrounded by family and love. She sensed that it would be easy to slip back into the pattern of those days.

She prayed that the time would be short until Anza called for her. She would have to fight for her independence, she knew. It would be more difficult each day to keep from returning to the dutiful daughter's role.

She shook herself mentally as her boxes and furnishings from the little *adobe* house were brought in. She had sewing to do before she could leave. She must keep herself as busy as possible to make the time pass faster and to keep from thinking of the long trip ahead—a trip beyond her imagination.

She would not be alone on the trip, she assured herself.

9

José and his love would always be with her. She would not break her promise to Anza. If he had not thought, her capable of continuing, he would not have sent her the clothes and supplies. If she kept her mind on this and worked hard, the time would pass. All arguments would fall on deaf ears.

The days slipped by and Feliciana felt herself being pushed back into the family's routine. True, it was good to know the girls were cared for while she and Josefa, the sewing girl, worked on the new clothes. Gratefully, she let Josefa make the new jackets and skirts. She watched carefully, though, for in the future she doubted she would have a Josefa to help her.

"So strong, so tightly woven," the sewing girl exclaimed over the dark brown material. "No cactus will tear this."

At last the sewing was finished and still no word from Anza. August had passed, the month the expedition was supposed to have left, and now it was past the middle of September.

Rumors circulated of trouble at Tubac, where the rest of the colonists waited. Gradually Feliciana had met a few who would be her companions. As new people came into town, many had been identified as Anza people. So far they were only names to Feliciana: Félix, Valenzuela, Pico and Pacheco among others. Her mother had kept her from really getting acquainted with them.

While she waited, Feliciana's family grew even more insistent that she give up her plans.

"Stay, Feliciana. This is your home. Your children have friends here now."

It was true. The girls' enthusiasm for the trip was wearing thin. One morning Feliciana sat sewing by the open window. She could hear the girls as they played under the trees in the patio with her mother. She saw Rosita, the little kitchen maid, bring them their morning hot chocolate.

"This is so nice, *niñitas*," their grandmother was saying. "We are happy you are here with us. Why don't you stay? I'm sure the trip will be awfully hard—riding all day instead of a nice garden to play in and chocolate to drink."

"But *Abuela*," said Tomasa, "*Mamá* said she promised to go."

"That was when your poor *papá* was with you. Now she is all alone. She should stay here with her family and take good care of you."

"But—" Feliciana could hear the doubt in Tomasa's voice. "But she *would* take care of us wherever we are. She told us so."

"Tomasa, *querida*, of course she would. But it would be so hard for her, and if Indians came, what could she do?" Her mother's soothing voice angered Feliciana. "If your *mamá* insists on going, and I pray the Good God prevents this, you little ones could stay here safe with us until your *mamá* could come back for you."

Feliciana could stand it no longer, and she ran into the garden.

"*Mamá*, how can you do this to the children and me? They are my family and we will stay together." Bewildered by her angry tones, the girls ran and clung to her.

Feliciana forced herself to speak calmly. "I have talked about this with the girls. They know we may have trouble and that the trip will be hard, but we will be together. I would never leave them behind. Come, girls, let's go for a ride on Gallardo. He needs exercise."

Before her mother could protest, they had gone to find and saddle the horse. A brisk run restored Feliciana's good humor. Each day she had tried to find a time for the three of them to ride. Gallardo needed to be kept in good condition for the many weeks ahead.

As they rode, Feliciana again sounded out the girls' feelings about the trip.

"You don't have to come, Tomasa, if you would really rather stay with *Abuela*. It will be a long hard trip and you are only six years old. But there will be other children your age, *Capitán* Anza said, and I would like to keep our family together."

"Oh no, *Mamá*," Tomasa was emphatic. "We want to stay with you. Don't we, Eustaquía?"

Eustaquía nodded solemnly. She agreed with whatever Tomasa said.

"Someday we will have a garden with trees. I don't know where, but *Capitán* Anza says California is a beautiful place with many more trees than here. We have to trust him, *niñitas*."

As they came back to the Arballos's house, a strange horse was tied outside. Feliciana handed Eustaquía down to the boy who came for Gallardo. As she and Tomasa dismounted she heard her mother's voice from inside.

"No, *Señor*, I am quite sure. I don't think the *señora* is going to be riding with *el capitán* after all. It is too hard a trip for a young woman alone with two children. I don't think your message will interest her."

Puzzled, Feliciana stepped into the house. Her mother was speaking with a young soldier.

"And what message is it that will not interest me?" she asked her mother.' "Surely that is my business. And since when have I said I was not riding with the colonists?"

Her mother stammered, "Oh Feliciana. Here you are." A tall, handsome young man stepped forward with a bow.

"I am *Don* Francisco Muños. *Capitán* Anza asked me to see you. The expedition is to assemble on the Plaza de Horcasitas the morning of September 29, ready to travel. Mules will be sent the day before for loading. I gather you have your own horse?"

"*Sí, Señor*," said Feliciana. "Thank you, and *sí*, we will be ready to go." To herself she thought, you'll never know how ready we will be.

She saw his approval as he studied her intently while being shown to the door. She wondered if he was to accompany the colonists, and was answered as he turned to her mother.

"Do not fear because she is alone. There will be many of us who will wish to aid her." Turning again to Feliciana, he said, "I almost forgot to tell you that you will be sharing the tent of *Señor* Santiago Pico, his wife and seven children. You see," he added with a chuckle, "you will not be alone."

Feliciana thanked him. With another bow, he mounted his horse and was gone. Were there other men in the expedition as handsome as he, she wondered. Were they all married? Probably, for Anza wanted family colonists.

Somehow, though, Muños didn't strike her as a married man. Or was that wishful thinking? She blushed, astonished at her thoughts.

Her mother was wailing again. "Oh Feliciana, why must you be so stubborn? *Ai, ai,* does a mother never count?"

Feliciana ignored the outburst and led the girls to her room. Her mind was in turmoil. The twenty-ninth was only five days away. There was so much to be done—clothes to be washed, packed and everything in readiness.

"At last," she spoke aloud, "we are going. Oh, *niñitas,*" she hugged them to her, "now we are *really* packing to leave. I hope the time flies by. But we must help *Abuela* feel not so sad. And we must send word to your papa's family to come see us leave. Oh, so much to do!"

The days passed so swiftly, Feliciana was startled on the twenty-eighth when two mules were detached from a long line of animals and presented to her by a young muleteer.

"If your chests are ready, *Señora,* I shall pack them."

Feliciana indicated the ready ones. Sudden fear shook her—the trip was for real. She still could back out. Then her mother's cries strengthened Feliciana.

"Yes, *Señor,* these are ready. Hush, Mother, I shall never change my mind."

CHAPTER 3

The Plaza de Horcasitas was bedlam with the curses of muleteers, cryings of the relatives and shoutings of the soldiers on that Friday, September 29, 1775. Feliciana was already mounted, Tomasa behind, waiting for Eustaquía. Feliciana was dressed in her new brown suit which felt much too warm. For the start of the trip she had twisted her long dark hair into a bun at the back of her neck. On her head was her broad-brimmed riding hat tied under her chin. Outwardly she looked calm and even regal, but her head ached with fatigue and frustration. Gallardo, snorting, pawing and tossing his elegant chestnut head, echoed her feelings and turmoil.

Feliciana pleaded once more with her mother. "Please, *Mamacita*, give me Eustaquía. I want to settle her in front of me. Tomasa and I are waiting and ready. I'm sure the bugle will blow at any moment."

Señora Arballo hugged the four-year-old, kissing her repeatedly and weeping loudly. "Why are you doing this to me, you stubborn girl. I shall never see my grandchildren grow up. Indians will kill you. You will die on the desert. If you do get to San Francisco Bay—wherever that might be—you will live among savages. Oh, *Madre mía*, protect them on this foolish expedition." With the latter pleas to the Holy Mother, she reluctantly handed up the tired and bewildered Eustaquía.

"You know why I am doing this, *Mamacita*. We've talked much and I have no fears. Please, let's say goodbye in love, not anger. The brave *Capitán* Anza has been there. He knows the way and says the land is good, not like this barren area."

Eustaquía nestled against her mother in the saddle. She and six-year-old Tomasa were exhausted from the long day of prayers and sermons.

The bugle blew at last, signaling the start of this first expedition of colonists in 1775 from Sonora, Mexico, to San Francisco Bay in Alta California.

"*Vaya con Dios!*" rang over the *plaza* from those left behind.

"*Viva Dios y el Rey! Viva Anza! Viva California!*" shouted the colonists, waving and cheering. The two girls waved, caught up in the excitement that at last they were on their way.

Feliciana, too, turned and waved and waved. The parting was harder because it had been delayed so often. Five hundred horses awaiting Anza at Tubac had been stolen by the Apaches, the terrorists of the Indian tribes. It had taken Anza much time to replace them here in this impoverished section of Mexico. Thoughts of these Apaches suddenly threw Feliciana into a near panic. She almost yanked Gallardo out of line. Then the "*Viva California*" cries restored her trust in Anza and she and the girls were on their way.

Padre Font, the Franciscan traveling with them, had delayed the permission to start, saying only "the time is not right." At last he had set the day, but even so, there had been long petitions to *El Dios* for success for the expedition. These were followed by a lengthy sermon by Font. It was 4:30 PM when the bugle finally blew.

Feliciana held the wiggling child in front of her as Eustaquía twisted and turned, trying to see the hundreds of horses, mules and cattle following them.

"Look, *Mamá*, everyone has a yellow ribbon like we do," said Tomasa. "Even all the horses have ribbons just like Gallardo."

Eustaquía clapped her hands and echoed. "Gallardo has a ribbon." As if to show it, Gallardo twitched his ribbon-braided tail.

As the *plaza* faded into the dust behind them, Feliciana felt younger and younger. She smoothed down the new linen jacket over the matching skirt. With the dust she was leaving the accusations and frustrations behind.

15

When the family had ordered her to withdraw from the group, she had become stubborn. Now her spirits lifted, she was free at last.

She knew that word that a young widow in her twenties was traveling with them already had spread among the colonists. The fact that she had two small children added to the interest. Though *Padre* Font showed his displeasure along with some of the older women, Anza approved of her. Today he had promised her sorrowing family that he would see to her safety on the trip. The new land was going to need many with her courage, he said.

Once the expedition was out of sight of the town, they crossed the nearly dry river. Feliciana saw that Gallardo's feet merely made small splashes. She thought it must feel soothing to the animals who had stood waiting so long that day.

Anza gave the order to stop here for the night. Everyone was tired from the day-long ordeal. They would be fresh in the morning with no tedious prayers to slow them up, Feliciana hoped.

It would take time this first stop, she realized, to set up camp, eat and settle down for the night. She watched with the children as tents, carried by the mules, were erected. There was one for Anza, one for Font, and seven for the colonists. The other two, she was told, were for special needs, such as a hospital.

Feliciana saw that the arrangement of the tents in a large circle had been planned. Each had its own space in front for cooking and eating, and yet there was room in the center for talks by Anza or Font and even for singing or dancing.

Beyond them she saw the brush shelters where the soldiers and unmarried men would huddle in their cloaks and blankets. Behind them were the animals, guarded by shifts of muleteers and others.

"If you will watch the children, I will make the supper," *Señora* Jacinta Pico told Feliciana. The older boys had gathered firewood and from the saddle bags of the mules came *tortillas, frijoles* and dried fruit. Everyone was tired. The refried beans, enveloped in the *tortillas* disappeared rapidly.

As they sat eating supper, *Señor* Pico said, "I never thought this day would really come."

Feliciana spoke up. "I still don't understand why the king gave us all these things—blankets, clothes, shoes and even hair ribbons."

"I heard," said Pico, "that the viceroy in Mexico City wanted *Capitán* Anza to take a large number of families to start a *pueblo* near San Francisco Bay, as ordered by the king. The viceroy told King Carlos exactly what we would need for clothing and food."

"And the king sent all of this on one man's word?" Feliciana was startled.

"That's right, *Señora*. Anza made this trip last year, you know. If he says we'll need these blankets, for instance, I'll trust he knows why."

No one stayed up late, for morning would bring new experiences in packing tents and supplies onto the mules.

The Pico boys had smoothed out the dirt floor, removing small stones and sticks. Feliciana spread her sheepskin down in her curtained part of the tent. Eustaquía was asleep almost immediately, snuggled between Tomasa and her mother. Feliciana pulled up a large wool blanket, one of the four allotted to them, and settled herself for the night.

"*Mamá*," asked Tomasa in a small voice, "can I sleep next to you, too?"

"Of course, *niñita*." Feliciana made room for her on her other side. In the daylight the trip seemed a fun adventure, but now in the dark, fears became real. The two little girls needed warmth and closeness to reassure them. And she needed them, too, she realized. Had she been too stubborn? What was she doing, taking them so far from all they knew and those who loved them?

"Would you sing, *Mamá*, like you always do?" whispered Tomasa, interrupting Feliciana's worries.

"*Sí*, little one, but we must not disturb the others." So Feliciana sang softly the lullabies of her childhood. If they comforted the little ones, they took away her own gloomy thoughts.

When she stopped, a small voice came from another direction. "Thank you *Señora*. Please sing some more."

17

She sang on until all was quiet in the tent. Apparently others were having second thoughts about leaving home. Sleep came slowly to her. She thought of when Anza had come with his wonderful offers to those who would be willing to travel to the faraway land of California. There would be horses and mules, food for the trip and land for settlement when they arrived at San Francisco Bay.

Feliciana thought of the white petticoats, the serge skirt, the fine stockings and underthings packed in her box on the mule. another pair of shoes and a jacket were tucked away with the yellow dress and the dress she had worn at her wedding.

Besides these, were yards and yards of cloth for chemises, petticoats and dresses for the girls. All these had been the gift of the king. They would never in their lives have had such wealth had she *not* been stubborn!

Anza had stressed the wonderful California climate and soil. He spoke of the good life they would have in a short time. The young Gutiérrezes needed little encouragement. Forty families finally signed for the trip. But there were many who preferred the known privations at home to the perils of travel through Indian lands to a territory few had even heard about.

Feliciana had put away her private doubts about traveling without her husband. She talked with the girls about the hardships they might endure. She assured them they would be together and soon the expedition had become a great adventure. At last they were on their way. Cuddling a girl in each arm, Feliciana joined the rest in sleep.

CHAPTER 4

The bugle aroused the few still asleep the next morning. Refreshed, Feliciana hurried the girls into their clothes. They breakfasted on leftover *tortillas* and hot chocolate while the men took down the tents. Everything was fascinating to the children, who were in a holiday mood. It was slow work for the men, Feliciana saw, but she knew it would speed up as the days went by and they became more expert.

Tomasa, Eustaquía clinging to her hand, chattered with three of the Pico boys, Miguel, 7, Francisco, 6, and Patricio, 5. Little Antonia Tomasa and Josefa were babies and watched the older children with solemn big black eyes. Two older boys, José, 11, and Dolores, 12, were helping their father.

Finally it was time to start. Feliciana had just lifted Tomasa to her blanket behind the saddle, when a young soldier approached. It was *Don* Francisco Muños, the soldier she had met at her mother's home.

"After you mount, *Señora*, I will hand you the little one," he offered.

"*Muchas gracias, Señor*," she replied. She stepped up nimbly and settled herself in the side-saddle. Eustaquía held herself aloof from the soldier as he put her into her mother's arms.

"I'm happy to see you again, *Señora*. I shall be ready to help you whenever you need me."

Feliciana thanked him. He was certainly handsome and helpful, but she didn't want to get involved with any one man just yet.

19

"Ah, **Muños**," said *Señor* Pico, returning from loading the tent onto the mule. "I see you have beaten me in aiding our charming *señora. Gracias,* but she can count on me."

Muños bowed and left, a puzzled frown on his face. Feliciana wondered if he thought Pico was telling him it was "hands off" the young widow. After all, she was under Pico's care for the trip.

"Everything all right, *Doña* Feliciana?" Pico asked. "Young Muños considers himself quite a ladies' man. If you don't wish him to annoy you, just call me."

"*Gracias,*" she said. "He *has* been very kind but I don't wish to become involved so soon."

"Quite sensible, young lady. Anza assured us you were the type we would need in California. He speaks highly of you."

The bugle blew. "There is *Padre* Font behind Anza," Pico pointed out. "Font will lead us in the *Alabado* before we start each day. I understand he always rides just behind our *capitán.*"

The song, sung with great enthusiasm, passed from the front of the procession to the rear:

Thanks we give to thee, Great God,
And to your power praise.
You have permitted unto us
Body and soul to raise.

Once again the bugle sounded and the expedition was at last truly started. The group moved steadily, leaving the slow-moving pack animals and cattle behind. Often older children slipped from their horses and ran alongside to stretch their muscles, Feliciana noted. Anza rode from one end to the other, speaking to and encouraging those he passed.

Once, as he came by *Doña* Feliciana, he scooped Eustaquía from her seat in front of her mother and carried her in his arms for awhile. Eustaquía stared at him with her solemn black eyes. He ruffled the dark curls and whispered into her ear. The stolid little face broke into a sunny smile. She patted the ribbon in her hair.

"*Sí,* I like my ribbon." She pointed to her mother. Today Feliciana's hair again hung in a braid tied with a yellow

20

ribbon. "*Mamá* likes hers and so does Gallardo." She pointed to the horse also beside them. "Why do we all have ribbons?"

"That, *mi niñita,* is so I can tell who belongs to me. Would your mama let you ride to the head of the line and back with me?" Anza glanced at Feliciana.

"Please, *Mamá,* please," Eustaquía asked.

"Of course, and *gracias, Capitán.* She doesn't often take to strangers," she added. Feliciana was glad to be free of holding the little one. Tomasa was running just then with the Pico boys. The three of them were used to riding, but not for such long periods of time. They would have to get used to it, though, for there were many miles ahead.

She looked at the dry hard land around them. Only a few late desert flowers bloomed bravely. Patches of *galleta* grass and *mezquite* stretched in every direction. She was glad to be leaving, though it was hard to believe that California would not be like this.

When *el capitán* rode back, Eustaquía turned to Anza with a dazzling smile and kissed his rough cheek above the well-trimmed beard.

"If her children are as charming as she, California will become a wonderful place," he predicted as he handed her back to her mother. Suddenly Feliciana remembered old Juana's prediction about Eustaquía. She fingered the now cleansed thong around her neck and wondered what luck it possibly could bring.

Feliciana watched *Capitán* Juan Bautista de Anza ride on. She knew he was not yet forty, but already trusted to plan and make this extraordinary journey. Everyone liked him. Well, she thought, maybe not *Padre* Font. She knew the *capitán's* father had been a soldier and killed by the Apaches when his son was only two years old.

Anza was *comandante* of the small army post at Tubac where his family lived. The rest of the horses and cattle and ten more soldiers and families would join them there.

Eustaquía was chattering happily. "He nice man, *Mamá,*" she said. "He tell everybody I his little girl," she laughed. "But I your little girl, eh *Mamá*?"

Feliciana hugged her close. "Of course you are. You and Tomasa are special to me."

21

At the lunch break Muños, the young soldier, again appeared. Smiling, he reached up his arms to Eustaquía to put her down. "How's my girl now?"

Eustaquía drew back. "I not your girl. I Anza's girl." She pushed him away as he touched her. A scowl replaced the smile on his dark and usually attractive face.

"Thank you, *Señor* Muños for thinking of us. Eustaquía is tired and hungry. She's only four, you know. Let him put you down, Eustaquía. Then I'll get down and we'll have lunch."

After taking the still sulky child from the saddle, Muños turned to help Feliciana, but she had already stepped down.

She smiled up at him. "*Gracias*, but I'm used to doing this myself."

Muños was smiling again as he left. Feliciana was puzzled. Why should he be so upset by a small child? She sighed; maybe he was hungry, too.

Tomasa came running up with the Pico children, now good friends. So far the trip had been like a picnic, eating all their meals out-of-doors in nice weather. Feliciana knew, though, that it couldn't all be that pleasant, for Anza had warned them they would have bad days, too.

Señor Pico approached her as it was time to start again. "How good a rider is Tomasa?" he asked.

"A fine one, providing the horse is gentle. She rode often with her father."

"We have extra horses, you know. Anza had to find more when his at Tubac were stolen. One of these is mine. She is used to carrying my children. If you would like, Tomasa may ride her for the present. You could hold the reins, if you preferred."

Tomasa opened her eyes wide. "Please, *Mamá*." The six-year-old jumped up and down. "I get so tired riding behind you. I can't see anything."

Feliciana smiled. "You are most kind. For me, for Gallardo and especially for Tomasa, *muchas gracias*."

Señor Pico soon came back leading a small mare. He swung Tomasa onto the blanket serving as a saddle. "Hang onto her mane. Your *mamá* will hold the reins so you may ride beside her." He handed them to Feliciana, and remarked, "She is a capable little girl. You should be proud of her."

Feliciana's spirits soared. She had felt so alone as the caravan started, knowing she would have to earn the other colonists' respect. Already her girls were making their impact on the people who were important. She sighed. Because she was a widow and alone, *Padre* Font had already warned her to be "circumspect" in her actions. She felt he was constantly watching her.

Padre Font was a strange person, she reflected. He was so cross-looking, as though this whole trip was something to be endured. He didn't look well and rode as though he had never done so before. Rumors were that Anza had requested him to go because he was able to take readings from the sun and stars and would keep the expedition on the right course. He had been a *profesor*, which probably explained his pale complexion. Feliciana guessed he liked music, for he carried a small psaltery with him. Some said that the starting date had been delayed because Font wanted to start on his birthday. Feliciana noted that not many liked him.

Word was that *Padre* Garcés, who would join them at Tubac, was entirely different. A jolly and pleasant man, he often lived months at a time alone among the Indians. But Garcés was only going with them as far as the Colorado River. Feliciana wished it were the other way—that Garcés would stay with them, even though she had never met him.

CHAPTER 5

As the Picos and Feliciana sat around the fire that night, Anza came by and said they would remain there another day. The mules with the heavy supplies had fallen far behind and would catch up tomorrow. These mules carried gifts for the Indians they would meet, as well as munitions—which he hoped would not be needed until they reached California—and extra food supplies.

"Because of this delay, we shall have to travel a little faster in the next few days. As the mules become rested we will send them on ahead of us." Anza paused and smiled at the group. "You are good travelers. Tomorrow will be a fine day to get acquainted with each other. Sleep well," and he went on to the next campfire.

Feliciana was relieved. She ached in every muscle and bone. She had never ridden for such a long stretch before. The children could run at times, but the women were restricted.

Eustaquía had fussed and squirmed as the afternoon wore on. She finally fell asleep and when they had stopped at 4:30, Feliciana's arm was numb.

She noticed everyone was stretching and stamping feet. How the others slept that night she didn't know, but she was almost too tired to relax. She prayed for those left behind, for her little girls, and for Anza. She was grateful for his concern for them all. Perhaps waiting for the slow mules had been merely an excuse for the weary colonists to get their second wind. Her last prayer was that she could find strength to care for her girls and keep going. She would not be a quitter, although Anza had assured them that any who wished might still change their minds and turn back at Tubac. Then at last she fell into a restless sleep in which Gallardo kept trying to outrun the others, jolting her forward and backwards, and old Juana was calling "You are going to become famous."

The next day was visiting day. Feliciana and *Señora* Pico took the little ones to the neighboring campsites. There were some young families with only one or two children, while others had as many as nine. There would be more people joining them at Tubac, still two hundred miles away.

Some of the men, used to spending days in the saddle, grumbled at the delay, complaining there had been enough waiting around.

But then Anza hurried them on, and soon they had passed the mules. On the sixth of October they reached good pasturage by the sluggish river, and Anza decided to stay here for a day. Some of the loaded mules had strayed and he planned to send a few of the soldiers to find them.

Late that afternoon, Muños stopped by the Picos' tent and told Feliciana about it.

"We were out hunting the mules—*ay-ie*—what stubborn animals! They would get tangled in a mesquite bush and refuse to move. We had to drag each one out and hobble it until we had them all."

Feliciana laughed. "They probably don't like their loads. The harder you pull a mule, the more he digs his feet in. You have to coax them."

"With what?" asked Muños sourly. "Next time we'll take you along to do the coaxing. I think I'll hide the next time Anza orders mule hunting."

"Do you have to do this often? I thought that was the muleteers' job."

"Usually they only need the muleteers, but if I have to go, I'll remember to take you along." He gave her a half-smile and went on.

Feliciana had been singing not only to her own girls, but also to the Pico children. That night *Señora* Pico came to her.

"*Doña* Feliciana, a woman has started weeping nearby. Now some of the other women are joining her. I think they are realizing they might never return to their homes again.

Would you come and sing to them? Maybe to remind them they take their home with them?"

"Of course, *Señora*. I know. They are probably homesick."

Feliciana and *Señora* Pico went and sat with the women. Softly, Feliciana started singing the lullabies she sang to the children. Then she changed to an old well-known song from Spain, *El Trovador*. As she sang another, *Tus Ojos*, one by one the women joined her. Soon, Feliciana was conscious of a guitar and a man's voice blending with them. It was *Señor* Muños.

Tears were gone, Feliciana noticed, when the group broke up and went to their tents. The young soldier spoke:

"I hope I didn't spoil your singing. It would be good if all the people had these songfests. It's good to sing together. Maybe you could sing to the mules, too."

They laughed, Feliciana glad to see him restored to good humor.

After slipping into bed, she thought of Muños again. He and the other men without families had to sleep in the open. Maybe his changes in humor were due to some bad nights. He was charming when everything went smoothly. Perhaps he needed a wife to keep him happy. She smiled at her fantasies. At the moment she wasn't interested in marrying Muños or any other man she had seen so far.

CHAPTER 6

Feliciana wondered at the hurry of the next day's journey of six leagues, though she and the girls were getting used to continuous riding. The following day Anza halted the expedition at noon and asked heads of the families and the soldiers to attend a special meeting.

Feliciana and Jacinta Pico fed the children and sat waiting, relieved when *Señor* Pico returned. His expression was serious, Feliciana noticed. Not bad news, she hoped.

"Tomorrow we are to stay here and repack the mules," he said. "We are entering the long *cañon* of Ignacio, where there might be trouble with the Apaches."

Feliciana felt a sudden constriction at the word "Apaches." Pico went on: "We have been traveling up the valley of the Rio Magdalena. Now Anza wants to take a short cut through this *cañon* to Tubac.

"Since the mules have been overloaded with supplies, they have moved slowly. By shifting some of the load onto the extra horses, the men can move the pack animals a little faster, and perhaps avoid the Apaches."

"We'll all walk," offered Dolores, the oldest Pico boy. "Then there will be more horses."

"No, *niño*," his father answered. "*Capitán* Anza wants everyone to ride. We can double up some of the young ones, but he wants no children running loose for the next few days."

Feliciana struggled with her fear as Pico continued. "We will ride through the *cañon* in a special formation. Soldiers will be at the front and rear. Groups of people will ride between the horses, mules and cattle. We will be traveling a little slower as a result."

Señor Muños came alongside Feliciana that night. "I'll be riding behind you and your girls," he informed her. "Don't worry." He waved as he rode on. Feliciana felt the tension in her stomach ease a bit.

After supper, the women gathered in a group. Feliciana had noticed that several were far along in pregnancy. She wondered how they had had the courage to start out in that condition for the far unknown. Tonight the women were discussing plans for helping *Señora* Félix, should her labor pains start in the next few days.

"Nonsense," pooh-poohed the *señora*. "I have had seven little ones already. Why should another one upset the *capitán's* plans?" After a moment she added with a wry smile, "I hope I can wait until we are through the *cañon* though, and no Indians are around." It was a thought they all echoed, Feliciana was sure.

She had planned from the beginning to show no fears. But having Muños assure her he would be nearby had surprised her with a feeling of relief. Was she always going to want a man nearby for emergencies? *Had* she been wise to join Anza's expedition?

Again the women all sang with Feliciana, softly this time, hoping no scouting Indian was nearby. Anza had assured them he doubted there would be any trouble, for mostly Indians tried to run off the animals. With the mules and horses scattered among them, there would be no stragglers to tempt the Apaches.

As the group separated for the night, no one spoke of the fears she was having, but each cheerfully called, "*Buenas noches.*"

Tomasa clung fearfully to Feliciana as she settled herself between the girls. "Are there really Indians out there?"

"*Sí, niñita,* but you are not to worry." Feliciana held her closely. "There are Indians all over these lands. They have always lived here—it is their homeland. They are just like all people. Most will step aside, curious as to what we look like. At home, you know, there are bad people who rob and beat others. Just so, there are Indians who are cruel, even to other Indians."

Feliciana had decided from the beginning to be honest

with the children, especially Tomasa, who took life seriously. Their fears were hers also. However, she didn't think it necessary to tell them she had heard that Indians usually attacked at night.

"The boys are saying how cruel Indians can be. I'm scared, *Mamá*."

"I am too, Tomasa, but I trust the good God will guide Anza and us through this *cañon* safely. Now go to sleep, *niñita*. We are in *El Dios'* care."

To herself, though, she wondered what she could do to protect the girls. She had told her mother that she would look after them, but there was no place to run to or hide in this boxed-in *cañon*. Would the Indians attack from the rear or shoot down at them from the ridges?

Feliciana was sure others must be thinking the same way. Lovingly, she held the girls closer and sang to all in the tent.

For each of the next three days they could only make four leagues a day. Shrub-covered walls towered high above them. Along with the others, Feliciana searched the hillsides for a tell-tale movement. Once she thought she saw an Indian head peek out from around a large rock. It didn't help to hear the wild imaginings of the boys.

"Look there, over to your left!"

"What's that up there—behind that bush near the rock?"

Eleven-year-old José Pico laughed. Tomasa's fear-filled eyes looked everywhere he pointed. They were riding on his horse and she clutched him in terror, looking to her mother for comfort.

As they camped that night, still in formation, Anza walked among them. "Tomorrow, boys, let's not play games," he chided gently. "You are worrying the other children and women needlessly."

Some of the boys, including José, exchanged sheepish grins.

"OK, but girls sure scare easily," one said.

Darkness descended early in the *cañon*. With it came new sounds and fears: soft scurryings among the shrubs, birds settling for the night. Each sound was magnified in the dark.

29

Feliciana, with the girls huddled close, listened and wondered. Could that have been an Indian step outside the tent? She raised up to listen better. An owl hooted up the *cañon* wall—or was that an owl? She knew Indians often gave such sounds as signals.

From the restless movements and low murmurings within the tent, Feliciana knew that others were also awake. Tomasa pulled the blanket over her head while Eustaquía slept, unaware of the tensions around her.

Feliciana prayed the night would pass quickly. Suddenly she realized the step outside was one of the guards checking each tent. That reminded her that Muños was posted close by. Maybe that had been his step. She didn't feel so alone anymore. He really was a handsome man with his black hair and dark eyes under heavy eyebrows. As she drifted into sleep, the thought occurred that maybe he might become more than a friend before the trip was over.

The next nights passed more restfully than the first had. Then suddenly it was the last day. Feliciana awoke, rejoicing with the others. *Padre* Font and the colonists sang the *Alabado* with great feeling. She knew it was the last of the *cañon* and they covered eight leagues that day, for there was no waiting for the slower animals.

When Anza told them that night they would be in Tubac the next day, Feliciana sighed with relief. Tubac, the northernmost post, was Anza's home. Here, she knew, they were to stay for a week before the main journey began.

On Sunday camp was cleared quicker than usual. Even the mules seemed more cooperative. Feliciana, as well as the children, loved watching the muleteers loading them. First a sheepskin was thrown over the mule's back to prevent sores. The pack saddle was cinched tight over this. Here, the muleteers explained, they had to put a foot against the animal's ribs to keep it from taking a large breath. If it succeeded, later the mule would let out the air and the saddle would slip, the load shifting to one side or the other. The mule groaned when the cinch was pulled tight, but it was only a token complaint. As soon as the load was adjusted, the groaning stopped.

Feliciana saw how carefully the large boxes were hung

from each side of the saddle. These held the cargo—tents, barrels of flour, corn, beans and other foodstuffs. Some held the goods for trade with the Indians. Too, there were the barrels of brandy so loudly protested by Font. Anza ignored the priest and Feliciana guessed there would be times it would be important to have it.

Once, during the day, Anza rode alongside Feliciana. "Not long now, *Señora,*" he said gaily.

Feliciana looked around. There was just more *mezquite* and tall giant cactus with arms beseeching the skies and lots of dusty land.

"Do you like it here?" she asked.

He smiled. "This is my home with my wife and children. The Apaches seldom bother us now, usually to annoy us or make raids on our horses. The worst we have had lately was the stealing of the five hundred horses I had gathered for the expedition. I don't think we will see the Indians for a long time, now."

"Do many people live here?" Feliciana asked. "Does your wife like you being gone months at a time?"

Anza shrugged. "No more than any other soldier's wife, I guess. But she doesn't complain and has many friends here. We have the Tumacácori mission close by, and another, San Xavier del Bac, just a few miles away."

"This seems so far from any other civilized places," Feliciana exclaimed. "Have you been here long?"

"Yes, and let's face it," Anza said gravely. "This *is* far from what you call civilization, but it will be our last Spanish settlement before California." Seeing the dismay on her face, he tried to reassure her. "Remember, we have all the supplies we will need, God willing, and we are moving out of the Apache territory. We will encounter mostly friendly, or at most indifferent, Indians the rest of the way.

"As to your other question, I have been *comandante* here since 1760," Anza said proudly.

"You must have been very young," said a surprised Feliciana.

"Yes, I was only in my twenties. But you grow up quickly here or else you don't survive. Really, *Señora,* I think this is a lovely place and I predict it will someday become a large city. I hope I can stay here many years."

When Anza rode on, Feliciana again looked at the land. She did hope California would prove better than this. She absentmindedly fingered the blue stone which she now wore outside her clothes. It was lovely whether it had any special magic or not. She thought that magic really depended on the people who wore or carried charms rather than on the objects themselves.

This charm of Juana's had brought many comments from people she didn't know. At least it brought her new friends. Here in Tubac maybe she would meet more new friends.

Then in the distance she thought she could see a white wall standing against the low rising hills. Tubac!

"Look, girls," she pointed, "I think that is Tubac just ahead."

TUBAC TO
COLORADO RIVER

Tumacácori

CHAPTER 7

Feliciana saw the *pueblo* with great relief. As they came to the small white *adobe* houses of Tubac, she saw her feelings reflected by the others. The small dwellings were scattered over the low rise before the high-walled fort.

Though dust lay everywhere in this high desert and gardens were sad looking, Tubac was a haven to Feliciana and the other homesick colonists, she noted.

Now she saw the solid wall that had shown high on the horizon. It surrounded the officer's quarters and the large *plaza.* Beyond the fort, she guessed, would be the *corral* for many horses—a magnet for marauding savages.

Feliciana shuddered, thinking of the women living here so exposed to the Apaches. She had seen the joyful reunion of *Capitán* Anza and his wife and wondered again at the courage of *Señora* Anza.

Padre Font had left the groups shortly before the colonists reached Tubac. Feliciana felt a reprieve from his constant concern with her behavior, and was glad he was to stay at the Mission Tumacácori for the week she would be at Tubac.

The next morning Anza walked by the Picos' tent with a small child in his arms. Eustaquía came running to him, but stopped abruptly when she saw the girl.

"Eustaquía, this is my María. On the road you are my borrowed little girl. My home is here and my María lives here with her *mamá.*"

Feliciana wondered if the four-year-old understood the difference between real and borrowed or pretend. But she saw Eustaquía smile happily as she answered, "I have a *mamá* too, but no *papá*. You my pertend *papá*. Can María play with me?"

Feliciana relaxed; a playmate was more important. Several times, though, she had heard Eustaquía explain, "I don't have a *papá*." Was the child really wanting one like the other children had?

So far, the only man Feliciana thought might be considered for such a role made Eustaquía unhappy when he was around. Well, there was time ahead and new people joining them in Tubac.

Anza was answering Eustaquía, breaking in on Feliciana's thoughts:

"*Sí*, for a little time. Then later you and your *mamá* and sister will come and visit my wife Ana at our house?" He glanced at Feliciana as he said this. She nodded. She would indeed like to meet the woman who must live here alone so much of the time.

That afternoon Anza came and took them inside the fort's wall to meet his wife. Feliciana looked around the small *adobe* house. It was large by frontier standards, but not what she expected for the *comandante*.

Señora Anza welcomed them warmly with the traditional greeting. "Come in. *Mi casa es su casa*."

Feliciana was immediately attracted to the small friendly woman. *Doña* Ana's smooth dark hair framed a round smiling face. She had a quiet manner that spoke of much patience and understanding.

Feliciana noted that the house had been made attractive in many ways. A fine colorful rug lay over the hard-packed dirt floor and there were many pictures on the walls of trees and rivers. In one corner was a small altar with a picture of the Holy Mother above.

The furniture was handmade, probably here in Tubac, Feliciana guessed. There was a long plain wooden table with stools for seats. Piles of folded rugs or blankets on the floor doubled for sitting or for a bed for a guest. Strings of drying red peppers gave color along the walls.

"How lovely," exclaimed Feliciana. "It looks so peaceful and quiet here. But how can you stand it, surrounded by Apaches as you are, while your husband is away. Aren't you ever frightened?"

36

"Oh, I'm not alone," *Señora* Anza protested. "If there is a sign of trouble, everyone comes into the fort. Also, I have many friends living here in the village, so I am not lonely.

"We don't have many luxuries, as you can see," *Doña* Ana went on. "Everything must be brought from Mexico City. We do have little *fiestas* from time to time. In fact to celebrate your arrival we are planning one while you are here."

"Oh, that's wonderful," Feliciana exclaimed. "You don't know how homesick and frightened some of our women have been. Just stopping here where others seem to live comfortably and unworried is a pleasure. A *fiesta* will send us on our way with renewed anticipation of what your husband has promised us."

"You people gave us a good excuse to have one," *Doña* Ana said. "You wonder at our courage living here, while we admire you women traveling so far from home to an unknown place."

Anza protested. "It's not unknown. I've been there and seen the missions already established by *Padre* Serra. Now I'll leave you ladies while I attend to some business."

Doña Ana made a long face. "See," she said resignedly, "he is gone for long periods, and then when he's home there's business to take care of. But it's wonderful to have him here." She turned to the children. "How do you girls like this adventure so far?"

Tomasa and Eustaquía had been playing with the Anza children. An Indian girl had brought them mugs of chocolate and a tray of sweet cakes. Feliciana could see Tomasa's eyes shine. No one else so far had been invited to the Anza's home that she knew of.

She smiled at *Señora* Anza. "If we could have a party like this everyday, it would be fun. We like to ride, but not all day. Sometimes *Mamá* lets us down to run for a little way." Tomasa picked up another *bollito* and gave one to Eustaquía.

"What can we do for the *fiesta*?" asked Feliciana.

"Nothing," the *comandante's* wife said. "This was planned before you got here. It would be fun to dress up. I know the king gave you new clothes, but didn't some of you bring treasured dresses along? Wear them if you like.

37

We enjoy a change, too. After the eating we can dance. We have two fine musicians here at the fort."

Although *Doña* Ana was older than she, Feliciana felt at home with her. She was as sensitive as her husband, planning this party to give the colonists a touch of home.

Feliciana said as much as she and the girls left. "*Señora* Anza, the people of the expedition think your husband is a wonderful person. Now they will know why when they meet you at the *fiesta. Muchas gracias* and God bless you."

FIESTA! Feliciana had been thrilled when *Doña* Ana had told her about the coming event. Now, the magic word spread among the colonists like a grass fire. There was much to do. The children splashed in the nearly dry Santa Cruz River while Feliciana and the other mothers washed clothes. White petticoats sunned and bleached on the *mezquite* bushes, looking like great white birds.

Then they opened the saddle bags packed so carefully. They had not expected to do this until the end of the long journey. Carefully folded precious dresses were shaken out. Each woman had brought along something of her past—a comb, a *rebozo*, a *mantilla*—to be passed on to her daughters and granddaughters as a reminder of life in Mexico. Even the men found jackets and bright sashes to wear.

Feliciana spread out her soft yellow ruffled dress. Many months had passed since she had attended a dance. It brought back memories—sweet and sad—of the last festive party before her husband's death. She slipped on the dress, still unsure if now was the time to wear it.

She appealed to *Doña* Jacinta. "Would this look all right? Perhaps it will make me look too young and improper?"

"Nonsense," the older woman said. "The people of Tubac are doing us this honor. You have left your old life behind. We should respond, for I imagine they have few celebrations. Yes, Feliciana, wear the dress and enjoy the party. See," she pointed, "I'll even wear my best one, too, and the special *mantilla* that goes with it."

Feliciana thanked her. She brushed out her long lux-

38

uriant hair that she usually wore in braids on the trip. She caught it up with combs, letting the dark curls hang free. She felt years younger.

She saw that everyone had happily laid aside the coarse made-to-last clothes given them by the government. The people of Tubac appeared carrying great platters. Mouthwatering smells had been coming from the huge pit where a beef, butchered early that morning, had been placed over hot coals and covered with wet hides, hot stones and sand.

Long rough tables in the *plaza* held each *señora's* specialty. As Feliciana knew, this *fiesta* had been planned long before their arrival. *Capitán* Anza knew the lift it would give the travelers as well as those who lived here. Feliciana heard him laugh when he gave an order to one of his aides to unsling a brandy barrel, while remarking it was just as well *Padre* Font was staying at the Tumacácori mission.

CHAPTER 8

It was a colorful group that assembled on the *plaza*. Feliciana saw that the food was not much different than what they usually ate, but it tasted better shared in a party mood.

After everyone had eaten all he could hold, blankets to sit on were spread around the parade grounds. The night was warm and the stars glowed brighter and brighter as the darkness deepened. While the tables were removed, Feliciana and the girls found seats near the Picos.

Two men from the fort sat at one side with a flute and a violin. Two more musicians from the colonists joined them. After a short consultation they started a dance tune familiar to Feliciana—and to others, she noticed, as feet began tapping.

At first the people just sat and listened. Feliciana could hardly believe that somewhere beyond the fort hostile Indians might be lurking. She thought of what might happen if they suddenly attacked the partying fort. What could she do to protect her girls? Then she saw that the soldiers and their wives appeared unworried and she was sure guards were posted. She relaxed. Anza led his wife to the center to dance and gradually others joined them.

The music changed to a promenade. Men from both groups chose partners for the stately parade. Feliciana felt a touch on her shoulder. *Señor* Muños bowed and asked her to dance. She glanced at the children sitting with the Picos, and hesitantly rose. She had not danced since her husband's death and felt as though she was being untrue to him. *Doña* Jacinta nodded her approval, though, and as the dance continued Feliciana felt herself being especially favored. Not only was he one of the best-looking men there, but he danced superbly. She had seen his ease in the saddle and his touch on the guitar and wondered what other abilities he had. As the dance continued, she relaxed in this unexpected pleasure.

Muños gave way to another young man, and then it was a series of partners. She loved dancing and it was soon apparent that she was skilled. A beautiful young woman, a warm star-filled night and music from Old Spain—a thrilled Feliciana was surrounded by hopeful partners, as in days long past.

When the *fandango* started she was again dancing with Muños. One by one others cut in. Gradually the other dancers dropped out until only Feliciana and a young soldier from the fort were left. As the crowd clapped, the musicians played faster and faster. Feliciana whirled away from her partner and into her own version of the *fandango* as she had learned and danced it long ago. The mesmerized onlookers clapped and clapped until dancer and musicians stopped from exhaustion.

Tomasa rushed out and grabbed her. "*Mamá, Mamá,* I never saw you dance like that before. Will you teach me some day?"

Anza opened the brandy cask for the men, and cool drinks were served to the women. Francisco Muños handed a cup to Feliciana. There was no smile of approval on his face—only a scowl.

"That is no way for a decent woman to dance," he said.

"I have danced the *fandango* since I was a young girl. There is nothing wrong with it," Feliciana defended herself. "Thank you for the drink."

"I hope I never see you dance that way again," and he stomped off.

"Beautifully done, *Señora*," Anza came from behind her. "I knew we had a lovely singer, but not such an accomplished dancer. I shall remember this on the trip ahead. We may need to make small *fiestas* to keep up our spirits. Thank you *Doña* Feliciana," and Anza moved on to thank the musicians.

No one stirred, they were going nowhere tomorrow. The musicians started a familiar melody and happy voices joined them. Song after song filled the balmy desert air. Children dropped off to sleep on the blankets beside their mothers. Finally the tired musicians laid down their instruments and the families quietly gathered their little ones and headed to bed. Feliciana knew this had been a special night, perhaps never again to be repeated.

In *adobe* and tent fine clothes were set aside to be stored or repacked in the morning. There was no need for lullabies that night.

Tomasa sleepily hugged her mother. "You were so beautiful tonight, *Mamá*. You are the most beautiful person in all the world."

Feliciana held the sleepy children in her arms. She hoped she was more than a beautiful person. She would need courage and good judgment to care for them in the coming weeks. She was too keyed up herself to go to sleep quickly.

It had been the first dance since her husband José had died, and her first party. She felt a bit guilty because she had enjoyed it so much. Had she been wrong to dance the *fandango* alone? She had done it without thinking. Muños had disapproved but Anza thanked her. Why was she so upset at Muños's reaction? He had been helpful and thoughtful to her and the girls, though it was true Eustaquía disliked him. But he had no right to tell her what to do. Only a husband could do that, and she wanted no husband at this time, no matter how attractive he might appear.

As she dozed, she again remembered the brilliant stars, the music that set feet tapping and the warm feeling towards the people of Tubac who had planned this special evening for them. Softly, as though to put an amen to her thoughts, she heard a distant bell.

Not one bell, but four that rang softly, one after the other in a broken chime. How lovely, she thought. Then she came wide awake in a hurry. There were no bells here. She was not at home in Horcasitas. She waited, listening for the bells to ring again. Then the sound returned as though floating on a gentle breeze.

She listened and strained her ears, but heard them no more. Was I dreaming? she wondered. No one else in the tent had moved. A puzzle, but they had been like a benediction for the wonderful evening. She worried no more about the dancing and was soon asleep.

CHAPTER 9

Carefully Feliciana folded the party clothes and stowed them again in the saddle bags. Would she need them again on the trip? Someone stopped by the Picos' tent to report that *Señora* Félix was still feeling fine, but wishing to get this birth over while the colonists were resting.

"Poor soul," commented *Doña* Jacinta. "It would be so comforting to have it over with before we start again. I know Anza is worried at any delay. One of the families going with us from Tubac has not yet returned from a trip, so we are staying another day."

The two women now worked well together preparing the *tortillas* and beans and hot chocolate for the noon meal.

"I'm surprised at the courage these women had when they knew they were pregnant and were still willing to make the trip," said Feliciana.

"Probably they had little to say about it," said the older woman drily. "If the man wants to go, many times the woman is given no choice. It's a man's world, Feliciana. Look at them now." She pointed to where a group of men squatted in a circle exchanging tales as they waited for the next meal. "Of course they do work hard setting up camp and caring for the animals. But our work is the same, at home or on the expedition.

"Last night was a treat. You pleased everyone with your singing and dancing."

Feliciana laughed. "Not everyone. Francisco Muños told me I was immoral. Usually he is helpful and pleasant. And maybe *Padre* Font would not approve, he is such an unhappy-looking person. But last night was a beautiful time. Then when I heard the bells, I thought I was home in Horcasitas."

"What bells, Feliciana? Are there bells here? The mission is about two leagues away. But why would anyone ring them at that hour?"

"I thought I heard bells, four of them, in fact," Feliciana said. "They seemed to come from far away. Maybe I *was* dreaming. but it was such a nice ending for a happy evening."

After the noon meal, Feliciana turned to *Doña* Jacinta. "I think I shall take the girls and call on *Señora* Anza. She told me to come and see her. Perhaps she can tell me what bells I heard last night—if indeed I did hear some. Also I can thank her again for the *fiesta*."

Tomasa and Eustaquía were delighted to be going to visit their nice *capitán's* house and *Doña* Ana welcomed them warmly.

"We enjoyed you so much, *Doña* Feliciana, and your dancing is beautiful. It was a pleasure for us who live here. Sometimes it's hard to remember how other people live."

Again the little *dulces* and chocolate appeared, to the girls' delight.

"You'll spoil them," Feliciana protested. "I'm afraid they will not get such treatment for a long time. Thank you for the girls, and too, for the happy time we had last night.

"Also, I came to ask you, *Doña* Ana, are there bells that ring near here? I thought I heard some before I went to sleep last night."

"Bells?" asked Anza's wife. "Not here in Tubac. Tumacácori has one, but it is only rung for services and special occasions."

"Maybe I was dreaming then that I was home. They seemed like a benediction to a wonderful evening. I didn't think I had seen any, and no one else heard them." She laughed. "I start dreaming and forget which is real, but I thought I would ask."

After some woman-talk, Feliciana called the girls to start home.

"Thank you for the little sweetmeats and for setting me straight about the bells."

"What's that about bells?" asked Anza, coming in the door.

"Oh nothing, really," Feliciana said. "I was just asking if there were bells here. I thought I heard some after we had gone to bed. Now I know I was dreaming."

Anza had a peculiar expression on his face. "Tell me about them. How many bells did you hear?"

Feliciana was puzzled. "I thought I heard four bells, only they didn't ring together. It was as though they had a sequence—one, three, two, then four. And back down again. But *Doña* Ana says there are no bells, so obviously I was dreaming."

"Perhaps yes and perhaps no," replied Anza. He smiled enigmatically. "Would you like to hear a story about some lost bells that is told in these parts? It's an interesting mystery. I'll come by after supper."

"Lost bells!" exclaimed Tomasa on the way home. "How could anyone lose bells?"

"Did you hear any last night after we went to bed?"

"No, *Mamá*." Tomasa was positive.

"I was probably dreaming of the bells at home. I always liked hearing them. Now let's hurry and help *Doña* Jacinta with supper."

When Anza arrived at the Picos' camp site, he saw an unusually large number had gathered. Tomasa had told the Pico boys, "Tonight *Capitán* Anza is going to tell us a mystery story about bells."

A story! Lost bells! A mystery story about bells—and probably Indians! The rumors grew and grew.

Anza started: "Now if I were to tell you that there are no bells except the one at Tumacácori, would you be satisfied?"

He laughed at their murmurs of disappointment.

"You said lost bells, *Señor*," one of the boys called out.

"And so I did," agreed Anza. "Mind you, I cannot vouch for the story, but part of it *is* true. You can believe the rest as you wish."

Feliciana became self-conscious. Could *she* have heard those "lost bells" she wondered. She listened carefully as Anza went on. "It starts with the Jesuit *Padre* Eusebio Francisco Kino, whom I'm sure you all have heard of."

45

Many of the elders nodded their heads.

Anza went on. "He came from Austria. He had been ill as a young man and his doctors weren't sure they could cure him. Kino prayed to his patron saint, Francisco Xavier, to aid his doctors. He recovered and decided to spend the rest of his life in missionary work. He asked to be sent to China, but was ordered to Mexico instead.

"The Jesuits gave him the territory here in the northern part. He was the only white man among all the Indians in this area. He wasn't afraid of them and mostly they trusted and helped him."

"Like *Padre* Garcés does?" asked one of the men.

"That's right. He even built his first little missions by himself. When two more *padres* joined him, they started three more, all in the Sonora area.

"Then they came north and built Tumacácori where *Padre* Font is staying. Mission San Xavier del Bac is just a little way beyond us and Kino dedicated that one to his patron saint. Garcés makes his headquarters there."

"*Capitán* Anza," Feliciana broke in, "have the Apaches continued to bother the missions? Are they apt to try to frighten our expedition? We aren't all as courageous as *Padre* Kino was. Do they know we are going on and not staying here?"

"Yes, I'm sure they know we are moving on," Anza answered. "And yes, they did continue to annoy the missions. Having just stolen our horses, I doubt we will have any trouble.

"About that time Spain ordered all the Jesuits home, and soon the Franciscan *padres* came in their place. Now, as you mentioned, *Padre* Garcés travels free and unafraid among the Indians.

"But back to the bells. This story was passed on by the Jesuits when they left. Sometime, no one knows when or how, four special bells that had been cast in Spain before Columbus came to the new land were delivered and hung in the bell tower at Tumacácori. Each rang a different tone. The two *padres* learned to ring them in a pattern of one, three, two, and four. Then they rang the bells in reverse."

José Pico nudged his friend Cipriano. "That's what

Tomasa said her mother heard!" The boys leaned closer to hear more.

"When the two Jesuit *padres* were ordered to leave, they knew no one would be coming to replace them for a long time. They were afraid the no-longer friendly Indians would steal all they could. So they gave away everything to the greedy savages until only the building was left. But the bells still hung."

"Didn't the Indians want them?" asked another listener?"

"Probably the *padres* thought they were too valuable, I'd guess," said Anza. "When new men came, they would be glad to have the bells. They discussed the problem and then sent the workers home. They wanted no witnesses among the Indians.

"The story goes that in the night the two men struggled to lower the bells and carry them, one at a time, far into the desert. Somewhere out there," Anza gestured beyond them, "they buried the bells in the sand in the order of their ringing. If they left any records of where the bells were, no one knows."

Anza paused a moment. "This is the mystery. Sometimes, on a still night when there is little wind and the stars are brilliant, travelers say they can hear the bells, always rung in their right order. I have lived here many years and have never heard them. That's not saying no one has," and he looked at Feliciana.

"Did anybody hunt for them?" asked one of the teenagers.

"Oh yes, many have hunted." He laughed. "Want to hear another good story? This has been told around at each mission and *pueblo*. It seems one day an old prospector staggered into Tubac. He was exhausted and asked for water. He was dirty, his clothes ragged and he hadn't shaved in days. In his hand he held a crumpled bit of old paper. On it, he claimed, were the directions for finding the lost bells.

"He offered to exchange it for a drink, saying he was too tired to hunt any longer. Men rushed to the desert, digging frantically with any tool at hand in any spot that appeared similar to the directions.

"Suddenly a shovel struck metal. Renewed efforts at last uncovered an old bucket. Those digging thought they heard muffled laughter from near some greasewood in the distance. However, they never found out who had played the trick."

Feliciana laughed with the others.

Anza became serious. "You may stay up all night listening for the bells, if you wish, but on no condition will anyone be allowed to wander into the desert. Remember, Indians have scouts out at all times, especially when there is a large gathering as we have here tonight. They will not disturb us, but a lone boy or two would be asking for trouble."

The next morning no one was able to say he had heard the bells. But José Pico said, "There's still another night yet."

Feliciana was sure now that she had been dreaming when she thought she had heard the sound of bells on the quiet air. She refused to say anything more about them, although several questioned her. But Anza repeated his warning to the boys not to wander away from the fort.

Anza's caution was not needed. During the night Feliciana heard many strange sounds she couldn't identify, but definitely not bells. Coyotes, Indians, maybe, and certainly frightening to her. She was sure the boys were not really interested in looking for bells.

CHAPTER 10

During the *fiesta* and since, Feliciana had met most of the Tubac families that were joining the expedition. The missing officer and his family had returned. She guessed they were frantically finishing their packing.

Since Feliciana was ready, she and the girls took a walk to the fort to say goodby to *Señora* Anza. She wasn't home at the time, so they continued walking past other homes.

"Look, *Mamá*," said Tomasa. "Those people are packing some mules. Maybe they are going with us. What's that girl carrying?"

Feliciana had noticed the men and mules. Then she saw the girl—a little older than Tomasa, probably.

"Why, I think she has a cat and some kittens in a cage. I wonder if she is taking them to a friend to keep. Surely the cats aren't going with us." Feliciana could picture a frantic mother cat chasing her kittens, who wanted to run in all directions. She laughed to herself. She also had two child-kittens who were tempted to run at times.

"Could I go talk to her, *Mamá*?" asked Tomasa.

"*Sí*, but don't visit too long. I'm sure they are all busy."

"I'm Tomasa Gutiérrez," she said, going closer to see what was in the cage. "Are you going with *Capitán* Anza too?"

"*Sí*. I'm Gertrudis Peralta. My father is a corporal here in Tubac."

"Are your kittens going too?"

"*Sí*. My mother almost didn't let me bring them," Gertrudis confided. "I promised to take good care of them. We mustn't hold the babies much yet," she said. "They were born only a few days ago. The mama's name is Luisa, but I haven't named the babies yet."

"I'm going to walk on for a few minutes, Tomasa," Feliciana said. "Then I'll be back for you. It's almost time to eat."

Eustaquía was clinging to Tomasa. No danger of this kitten running off right now. It was safe to leave them here inside the walls and it was good for Tomasa to find another girl to play with. José often let her ride with him, but mostly he was off with the many boys.

Soon she collected the girls, who were bubbling over the kittens. As they ate, Tomasa told the group, "You should see Gertrudis's kittens. They are so tiny and make funny little noises. Then the mother cat comes running to them."

"Why is she bringing them with her?" Feliciana asked.

"Gertrudis's mama didn't want her to bring them. But the new people coming to their house were going to drown the kittens, she said. Isn't that awful? They are going to ride on the mule and stay in the Peraltas' tent at night. Gertrudis let us touch them for just a minute."

"Soft, *Mamá*, soft," Eustaquía said happily.

"Gertrudis's tent is going to be near ours," Tomasa said happily. "She said we could pet the kittens every day. Now the trip will be much better."

At bedtime the girls were still excited about their new friend. Feliciana had to shush them more than once, reminding them that they were leaving in the morning and must get to sleep. There were more songs than usual that night.

The morning of October 23, 1775, saw the expedition getting ready with far less confusion than when it had left Horcasitas. Feliciana and the other seasoned travelers watched as Anza had a conference with a tall young lieutenant about Anza's age. They learned he was *Don* José Joaquín Moraga, second in charge to Anza. He had just finished organizing the Tubac group to start.

As Feliciana studied him, *Señora* Pico commented, "He hardly seems to be the man to second Anza. But he has worked with him for a long time, so he must be capable.

He is so soft-spoken, though—it makes you wonder."

Feliciana saw Moraga and a few men ride on ahead. Anza started off at the sound of the bugle, with Font behind, leading with the *Alabado.*

At noon Feliciana saw the lieutenant and his men return. Later Pico explained, "The men went ahead to check on the wells. Sometimes, according to Anza, we will have plenty of water, and other times it will be scarce. This time Moraga reported the wells are full."

Anza halted the group at four o'clock. *Señora* Félix had started labor. The *capitán* set up the special tent for her; this would be used when anyone became ill.

Feliciana and the others ate a quiet supper. At nine Anza emerged from the tent with the welcome news: "A lusty boy has joined us."

"I'm so glad for her," Feliciana said to *Doña* Jacinta.

"I, too, am relieved. At least she will have the night to rest. Perhaps she can delay and come on with the pack animals later."

Early the next morning men's voices and unusual activities awakened Feliciana and the Picos. Hastily they dressed and went outside. A dismal grey overcast greeted them. They watched *Padre* Garcés, who had joined them at Tubac, mount his horse and set off northward by the river. A wagon carrying a rough coffin and pulled by mules followed the *padre,* with four soldiers bringing up the rear. Feliciana saw that one of the soldiers was *Señor* Muños. She had not seen him since the *fiesta.* Had he lost interest in her because of her dancing? A sudden depression seized her.

She joined the women who had crowded around Anza and were showering him with questions.

"What has happened?" "Who has died?" "Where are they taking the coffin?"

Anza held up his hand for silence. "*Señora* Félix died of complications this morning. We did all we knew how for her, but it was not enough. The men are taking the body to Mission San Xavier del Bac for burial."

"What about the baby?" came from all sides. "Will *Señor* Félix stay with us?"

"The baby is fine and one of the young mothers has

51

taken over his care. *Señor* Félix says he and his family will continue with us."

A light rain started to fall. Though she had not known the woman well, her feeling of depression grew stronger. One had died and they had hardly started. The one man who had seemed particularly interested in her had apparently dropped her.

Feliciana noticed that Tomasa was unusually quiet and withdrawn that day. As they settled into bed that night Tomasa spoke up: "What would happen to Eustaquía and me if you died, *Mamá*?"

"I'm not going to die, *mi niñita*, she said. "But if for some reason that should happen, I know *Señora* Pico would love and care for you. It is too bad about the *Señora* Félix, but sometimes that happens, even if the mothers are in their homes. This little baby is fine and will be well-loved. His father will have to work extra hard on this trip to see that his children have lots of love."

"But I couldn't stand it if you died," Tomasa cried.

"But you would, because you are that kind of girl. You are like me. I didn't quit when your *papá* died. I wanted to—" she felt Tomasa start and turn towards her. "Yes, it would have been easy to just stay with my family. But I had promised to go on this trip, and I do what I promise. I am not going to die, and I don't think many others are either."

What the future would bring, Feliciana could not foresee. It was enough tonight to set Tomasa's mind at ease. There were loving people in the expedition who would care for those in need.

In the morning Anza delayed the colonists' start for San Xavier del Bac mission until afternoon. The evening before he had explained to the group:

"We have only a short way to travel in the morning, but the nearest *pueblo*, the Pueblito de Tucson, is too small to provide for us overnight. We will move on right after the service. Such a large group puts too much importance on the small *pueblo* and might attract the Apaches. They patrol this area regularly. The Indians here are friendly, but they too suffer from the renegade natives."

Feliciana gave a start when he spoke of the natives. She had been lulled into a sense of security while in Tubac. Would they ever be free of these Indians?

Anza went on, "Most missions were started with rough log and brush shelters. But San Xavier was special to *Padre* Kino, for it was named for his patron saint. He saw this lovely valley not far from the Tucson *pueblo* and decided this mission should be larger and better than the others. Incidentally, Bac is protected by the garrison at Tubac.

"The Pimas were always happy to please him. They brought large stones and boulders from the hills for the foundation. They made and laid the *adobe* brick on this. *Padre* Kino didn't live to see it finished, but the Indians and other *padres* continued the work."

"Were the Tubac soldiers always able to protect this mission?" asked Pico. "It seems so far away. How would Tubac men know in time to help here?"

"Unfortunately, about eight years ago the Apaches thought they had waited long enough. They swooped down one night and destroyed the mission, leaving only charred walls and the foundation."

Feliciana was most disturbed. "Didn't anybody come to help?"

Anza spoke slowly and sadly. "No. A few from the Tucson *pueblo* sneaked around the rampaging Apaches to ask our help. But we had only fifty soldiers and we were fifteen leagues away. If we had come, we would have been too late. Perhaps some Apache scouts, seeing us leave, might have directed the raiders against Tubac. It was a hard choice to make."

Feliciana was wondering why another fort had not been established; Anza went on, almost as though he had been reading her mind:

"I have learned that the garrison at Tubac is soon to be enlarged and moved two leagues nearer Bac. It will be located on the exact spot where the Apaches have gathered before each raid. Perhaps this will deter them. Then we shall have a better chance to guard both missions."

Feliciana hoped she would be far away if such an emergency over occurred.

When they arrived at San Xavier del Bac mission the next day, she was again amazed at the men who lived in these desolate areas with no protection. The burnt *adobe* brick had been repaired. New walls showed how large this would someday be. The chapel was finished and services were held there regularly for the Indians.

Padre Garcés led the service. Though he was a short untidy man, he had a face that glowed with love and understanding. He spoke in both Spanish and Indian dialect. Death, after all, he said, paid no attention to race or color, and *El Dios* loved them all.

Shortly after they had resumed the trip, Moraga and some of the rest of his men met them. Feliciana was near enough to hear him say, "All is well, *Capitán*. There are many good wells. Some of these fill with blowing sand, but we had no difficulty digging them out. The people must be careful though, and not waste the water."

After supper Anza repeated Moraga's report and added, "We will not water all the animals at the same time. Let the horses drink a little first thing in the morning and then water them again just before we leave."

Later, while Feliciana was sitting by the fire, some of the boys came to see *Señor* Pico.

"Stay away from *Capitán* Anza. He is very angry. Two of the muleteers have run away. Where would they go?"

"Probably they wanted to return to their homes," said Pico. "This is hard work for them. It's bad, though, for the Indians to know some are deserting."

When Anza came on his nightly check of the camp, he had no smile, though he greeted everyone politely.

Feliciana saw a new Anza. Everyone knew of his concerned interest in them, his care of the children and any who needed help. Tonight, however, the camp was subdued. It had lost its pre-Tubac lightheartedness. What is going to happen next, she wondered.

CHAPTER 11

The next day a guard shouted a warning about 1 PM. It was Friday, October 27, and they had gone about five leagues. Riders were seen coming from the east. Dust partially disguised their approach, and Feliciana hastily called her children close to hand.

Indians? The Pimas they had just passed were friendly enough. Could this be some Apaches off their regular trail?

Eustaquía and Tomasa clung to their mother, sensing the adults' fear. Feliciana and the Picos shooed the children behind a large *mezquite* bush. There was no other place to hide.

José Pico peeked out and reported. "The riders have stopped and are talking to Anza."

"Are they Indians? Can you tell which ones?"

José pushed his head out farther, thorns from the *mezquite* catching his hair and clothes.

"It looks like six—no, seven men. Oh-oh. One of them is tied and is a prisoner. I think the others are Pimas."

Señor Pico pushed his son back. "I'll go and see, but the rest of you wait here." José and his older brother followed a little way behind him, in spite of their father's order.

"Are these Indians after us?" Tomasa turned a worried face to her mother.

"I hardly think six Indians are going to bother us, Tomasa. No doubt these are friendly ones."

José and his brother came racing back. "The Pimas have one of the muleteers who ran away. Anza has ordered him beaten."

"Oh no," exclaimed Feliciana. "He wouldn't do that."

55

"But he did. I heard him," José said.

"But he is so kind. He would understand the man ran away because he's afraid of what's ahead." Feliciana was puzzled. This was not the man whom Eustaquía adored; who worried over the *Señora* Félix and then her family. Surely José had misunderstood.

"The *niño* is correct, *Doña* Feliciana," said Santiago Pico from behind his son. "*Capitán* Anza must maintain discipline. If he isn't strict with this man, others will leave when the going gets rough."

"But beating a man just for that is cruel." Feliciana, used to a small *rancho* dependent on a few faithful Indian servants, could not comprehend the necessity for a beating.

Pico broke in on her thoughts: "Perhaps it would be better if you women and the children stayed away from the *capitán's* soldiers right now. What is to be done must be done immediately."

There was no place to go far enough to get away from the man's cries. Anza ordered camp made here, as the pasturage was good.

This had not been a good week, Feliciana thought. Food was prepared with little talk. The boys, who had gone to watch the beating, were subdued.

There was no gathering for singing that night. Instead, Feliciana sang quietly to her girls and the others in the tent.

"Will the Indians find the other man who ran away?" asked Tomasa. "Will he be beaten too? It might make him stubborn and he wouldn't work very hard. He might even make trouble sometime."

"We'll have to wait and see. Army rules are different from the way we lived. He was hired to do work and he ran away. I think he knew he would be punished if he was caught. Maybe *Capitán* Anza wanted to impress all the men that this is a serious trip. Now, go to sleep, *niñitas*. We can't tell the leader how to do his work."

"He wouldn't spank us, would he?" asked Tomasa.

Feliciana laughed softly. "No *niñita*. I think he will leave that to the mothers and fathers. Now, mind me—I said no more talking. It's time to go to sleep."

56

The next day was one Feliciana never forgot. It started as most of the others had, pleasant weather and no change in the scenery. Frequently they passed small Indian settlements, but no one had seemed hostile. Once Feliciana saw the men pushing the women and children into their huts, out of sight of the foreigners. Sometimes curious dark eyes peeked through the brush shelters, delighting Tomasa and Eustaquía.

Often as they traveled the flat lands, the older children of the colonists ran free. They played tag around the horses, laughing and yelling.

Eustaquía had looked longingly at Tomasa and Gertrudis. "Can't I get down too, *Mamá*?" she asked today. Feliciana knew how Eustaquía was feeling. She too would love to be free of the saddle. She looked around carefully. They were between the long scraggly line of the colonists and the cattle that were some distance behind them, but she saw nothing else.

"All right, Eustaquía, and I'll get down too." Stopping Gallardo, she lowered Eustaquía to the ground by her hands, and then dismounted herself. She dropped Gallardo's reins, knowing he wouldn't wander.

By this time the colonists ahead were so obscured by the dust they raised, all she could see were the playing children. Tomasa came back for Eustaquía and they skipped ahead to the others.

The day was pleasantly warm and Feliciana enjoyed the walking, free of the dust ahead. She daydreamed a bit, wondering how far away were the rivers and mountains they must cross, but today was delightful—until Eustaquía screamed. Feliciana came out of her reverie to find herself almost surrounded by Indian men.

Eustaquía screamed again as she tried to squeeze between two of the men to get to her mother. Feliciana reached for her hand and picked her up. Frantically looking around, she saw no colonists, only dust clouds.

One of the men came closer, and Eustaquía screamed even louder as he reached out for Feliciana's blue stone charm. His grunt brought the others crowding close to her. Feliciana felt their greasy unwashed sweaty bodies pushing her backwards toward some brush shelters. She,

too, screamed hysterically as one man tried to take Eustaquía from her. Surely one of the colonists must hear her,
she prayed!

As she tried to push them away, without success, she
heard Tomasa and Gertrudis yelling, "Help! Help! Somebody help us!" Then Gallardo's snorting moist nose
shoved the men aside, and two more horses made wedges
in the ring of Indians.

"Feliciana!" a voice cried out, as she and Eustaquía were
suddenly lifted from the ground and placed on Gallardo's
back. "What are you doing here?" demanded *Señor*
Muños. "And why were you off your horse? Thank good-
ness I recognized Eustaquía's screeching!"

"Are you all right *Señora*?" asked *Padre* Garcés. "They
are usually gentle Indians." He turned to question them.

Feliciana's heart began to slow down. Tomasa and Gertrudis, still crying, came to pat Gallardo, who had gone to
the aid of his mistress.

Muños explained, "I heard the girls and told *Padre*
Garcés that I thought there was trouble. We couldn't see
you through the dust. Why did you fall so far behind?"

Padre Garcés patted her arm. "It was all a mistake," he
assured her. "That stone you wear is turquoise, a stone the
Indians believe brings good luck. They thought bringing
you into their tribe would bring them good food and
crops."

Feliciana's hand went to the charm Juana had given her.
What had Juana said? "This is for you to wear. But your
best good luck charms are your girls."

She looked at the abject Indian men. Without hesitation
she removed the thong from her neck and handed it to
Garcés.

"Please give the stone to them. My girls are my good
fortune. I really don't need this, and if they think it brings
good luck, then I want them to have it."

"You are a generous young woman," Garcés said. "Indeed you don't need symbols like this. Here, you hand it to
one of them. Word will travel that you must never be
molested, for you are the 'good luck' *señora*."

With as pleasant a smile as she could manage, she handed the turquoise to the nearest Indian, while *Padre* Garcés

explained her gesture. She did indeed hope it would help these poor people.

With great relief she turned Gallardo toward the trail. Muños lifted Tomasa to her seat behind Feliciana and put Gertrudis on his horse, and they hurried to join the rest of their friends.

"Thank you for coming so quickly, and with *Padre* Garcés especially," Feliciana said to Muños as he rode beside her.

"Better thank Eustaquía for her voice," he replied. "Tomasa and Gertrudis screamed too, and the other children ran to find their parents. For heaven's sake, woman, use your head, or all those so-called charms of your girls will do you no good."

As a subdued Feliciana ate supper that night, *Señora* Peralta came over to speak with her.

"Gertrudis told me of your ordeal today. I'm so relieved it turned out well. I guess we have all become a little lax when the children want down. Maybe it was a warning. *Padre* Garcés told us of your generous gift—at least I guess the Indians think of it as generous. I've heard that turquoise is valued highly by them."

"I'm sorry I let this happen," Feliciana said. "There was so much dust I never saw the Indian huts. *Padre* Garcés said the Indians told him they wanted to see a white woman up close. Then they saw the stone—and you know the rest. I'm sorry to have upset Gertrudis, but she and Tomasa helped with their yelling."

Feliciana relived the episode over and over that night. Eustaquía was restless and once called out in her sleep. Feliciana hoped the following days would be less hectic.

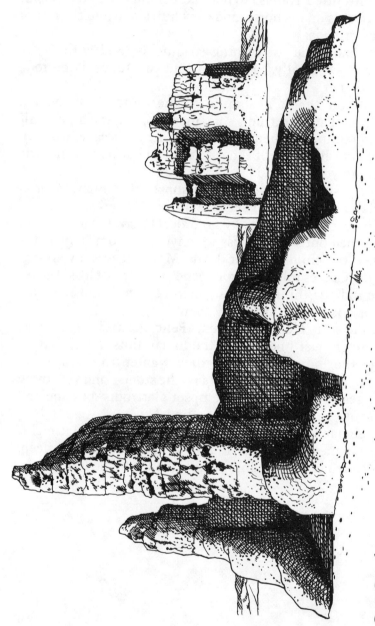

Casa Grande

CHAPTER 12

Feliciana heard early Sunday morning that Anza had sent four Pimas ahead to the tribes who lived by the Gila River. He wanted them to know a great group was coming and would be camped nearby for several days. Had he done this because of her problems with the Indians, Feliciana wondered?

"*Capitán* Anza says we have a long way to go today and tomorrow to reach the river," *Señor* Pico told his wife and Feliciana as they were preparing to break camp.

Instead, another shout from the rear guards brought everything to a halt. Four grinning Pimas came dragging the second runaway muleteer into camp. They knew *El Capitán* would reward them, Feliciana guessed.

The man looked in terrible condition; his clothes were torn and scratched as though he had been dragged through the bushes. Feliciana felt ill just looking at him. Surely he had been punished enough already.

But the same punishment was ordered. As she retreated into her tent, Feliciana hoped this would be a lesson to all and there would be no more desertions and beatings.

In view of the delay, *Padre* Font held a mass. Feliciana sighed. She was sure he would give a long sermon after the mass, and they were late already. In addition to fulfilling her prediction, he added a note of warning.

"There is to be no show of arms," Font said. "We must let these heathen know by our customs and actions that we come as friends. *Padre* Garcés guarantees these are kind and generous people, though their customs are different from ours."

Feliciana thought she saw a look of distaste on his face. She wondered what these new Indians were like.

61

When Font stopped, Anza spoke: "These heathen guard the crossings of the Gila and Colorado Rivers. Let's not antagonize them. As *Padre* Font said, all guns and weapons out of sight."

Camp was packed after a quick meal. Tomorrow would indeed be a long day.

They reached the good pasturage by the Gila River late on Monday. No one had complained at the extra-long day's ride, although Feliciana doubted she could have ridden another quarter league.

Anza stopped by their camp that night on his rounds.

"We are staying here tomorrow to rest and hunt for some pack animals lost in the desert shrubbery. Would any of you like to ride a little way further north in the morning to see an old Indian building that *Padre* Kino discovered? He named it Casa Grande."

Feliciana's face lit up; she had heard of this ruin before. After a night's rest, she was sure she would like to go.

"You go if you wish, Feliciana," *Señora* Pico urged. "I'm tired and will stay with the younger children. This is a lovely place to rest—just imagine, willow trees to look at."

"I'm tired now too, but I think I'll go anyway," Feliciana said.

She joined a small group in the morning who rode off with Anza. They headed for a tall mound that loomed high on the horizon.

Feliciana had mixed feelings when *Señor* Muños rode up beside her. "I should thank you again for rescuing me from those Indians," she said. She appreciated his coming so quickly, but still resented his criticism of her. "I haven't seen you for several days and wondred if you had ridden ahead."

"Oh, were you looking for me?" Muños asked in a bantering tone.

"Not particularly," Feliciana teased back. "Usually, though, I see you around somewhere and I wondered what you were doing."

"Lieutenant Moraga has kept me so busy running errands, I've not been with the group much. He picks on me all the time," Muños complained sourly. "Anyway, I was elsewhere when Anza sent men hunting the lost cattle and pack animals. And now I have a whole day with you," he added.

It took until noon to reach the mound, though in the clear air it appeared no more than a league away.

As they rode through the dusty dry land, Feliciana asked, "What's special about this Casa Grande? I've heard it spoken of at home almost in awe."

"I don't know much about it, either," Muños confessed. "It's been here for years, I understand, but no one lives here anymore."

The old mud structure sat on a knoll. They gathered with others around Anza when all had finally arrived.

"*Padre* Kino said this was probably built by the Hohokam Indians at least 200 years ago," he explained. "Kino thought their name was given them by the Pimas, because it is a Pima word meaning 'all washed up.' "

"What is this place? Was it for guarding the whole area or just their homes?" asked one of the men. It seemed to Feliciana that a warrior could have seen from the top of the walls for many leagues in all directions.

Anza went on: "Kino never found out. It could have been a fortress. See the long trenches leading to the Gila River? Perhaps they brought water from there for their crops. Maybe they had a long dry period and everyone died."

There were small holes in the upper section where one could look up. "Maybe they watched the stars," suggested another of the men.

They wandered around the huge structure made of the mud of the area. Feliciana saw that the winds and rain had already destroyed the original shape. She wondered about the people who had been here long ago—worked, played, lived and died—and no one knew why they had disappeared.

"Many come to see this building, called Casa Grande because it is the largest construction any of the Indians have ever seen." Anza said. "I thought you might like to see it, for it may be gone before any of you come back. Well—time to head to camp and see if the lost animals were found."

Feliciana wondered if she would ever come this way again. She doubted it.

"Why so quiet?" Muños asked after awhile.

"I was just thinking about the people who lived here and then suddenly vanished. They put lots of work into making the trenches for water and then it must have all dried up. It makes me wonder about where I'm going. Will I too just crumble away and no one remember me?"

"Don't worry about these dead people," Muños said. "I know where I'm going. I want lots of land and money. Then I'll be important and people will remember me."

Feliciana was irritated at Muños. "How do you know that you will always get what you want? Look at *Señora Félix*. She didn't plan on dying yet." Feliciana sighed. "I'm afraid I'm not in a cheerful mood today. Forgive me, but the future is so uncertain, and I get depressed."

Soberly, she rode on with Muños. There was no more conversation.

The warm welcome from the girls quickly changed her mood. Her normally happy disposition returned. Of course her family and those of the expedition were going to survive, because Anza had planned so well. The next exciting time she knew would be the meeting with the Yuma Indians, who would see them safely across the Colorado River. Garcés had explained one night that they knew the currents and the right time to cross. But if they didn't like you, you would never even be allowed to try. Feliciana shuddered—their fate should be decided in the next few days.

CHAPTER 13

They had gone about four leagues the next morning when Feliciana saw the Pico boys come racing back. They had been with the scouts in the lead, and she saw their father rein up sharply.

"Papá! Papá! There are some Indians coming! They have no clothes on, only daubs of paint. Their faces are streaked with colors—they look like they're on the warpath!"

Feliciana looked around nervously as Pico asked the boys, "What do the scouts say? Are they the Yumas Anza mentioned? He sent word for them to meet us."

Dolores shook his head sheepishly. "We didn't wait to hear what the scouts said. We've never seen natives like these before."

Almost immediately a tall Indian approached *Señor* Pico with a welcoming smile—at least Feliciana hoped it was a friendly smile. He held out a watermelon to them. Eustaquía screamed and Feliciana held her close, she herself almost in shock. Were the two *padres* right when they said these people were friendly?

The native was light-colored and completely naked except for daubs of mud and lines of red and blue paint on his body and face. There were several rings in his ears, and a feather through his nose.

Eustaquía clung to her mother, taking occasional peeks at this strange apparition. Another Indian approached carrying a watermelon, and a third native walked up with a large *ola* of water, which he set down near the road. He then came alongside Feliciana, to Eustaquía's continued distress, while Tomasa bravely peeked around her mother.

His hairdo fascinated them all. The long black hair had been plastered with mud and shaped into a tall mound high on his head. Some silvery powdered stuff had been sprinkled over it all.

The Yuma reached out to touch Feliciana's dark hair. She held as still as possible, though inwardly she shrank from his touch. He smiled and grunted, apparently pleased with her soft locks.

Padre Garcés came up and spoke a few gutteral words to the Yumas. Quickly they stepped aside and allowed the expedition to continue.

"Don't be afraid," he said. "They are friendly people and exceedingly generous. They know we must ride a little further to better pasturage. They grow these watermelons in great numbers, and have also brought us some wood for our fires."

At the next rest stop Feliciana watched as the melons were cut and distributed. Soon everyone was munching on their first fresh fruit in many weeks.

Eustaquía buried her nose into the soft pink-red flesh, as the sweet juice ran down her chin and arms. "Good, *Mamá*, good," she said, coming up for air and then diving in again.

"Where do they keep these, *Mamá*?" asked Tomasa. "They are so cool and sweet."

"*Capitán* Anza says that after the melons are ripe they are buried deep in the sand. The weather, hot or cold, can't spoil them. They have watermelons all year round. Want to live here?" she asked teasingly.

Both girls grunted their noes as they finished their share.

Refreshed, the group made good time to the pasturage. Feliciana and Jacinta marveled at the large plantings along the Gila River. On Friday they turned inland to a small lake which later Anza would call "Las Lagunas de Hospital." Here there was plenty of food for the animals.

Scarcely had they pitched the tents when, unexpectedly, heavy rain began falling. Now they were grateful for the wood the Yumas had brought. They cooked supper over smouldering fires and ate it inside the tents.

Señor Muños came by that evening to see how Feliciana and the girls were doing.

"We are staying here another day. One of the women is ill." He frowned at the sky. "I'm afraid we're in for more rain. Between the Apaches stealing our horses and *Padre* Font delaying our start, we are far behind the *capitán's* schedule."

"But will these rains continue long? At home what rain we had soon passed," Feliciana said.

"Not here," Muños replied. "Once we are across the rivers we will have even different weather. Wind, rain and snow will blow down from the Sierra."

"Surely it won't be too bad. Why are you so gloomy?"

"Have you ever seen snow?" asked Muños.

"No," admitted Feliciana.

"It is soft and white and floats down from the sky. It melts to water in your hand, and the air is bitter cold." Muños shook his head. "Once I was in a snowfall in the mountains and I thought I would never be warm again. I hope we escape the snow. We don't have the right clothes for it, for one thing."

"I hope so too. I don't think I would like cold weather." Feliciana thought of the warm sunny days and even hot ones in Horcasitas.

"If you need extra blankets, I'll try to find some for you," Muños offered. "Even the heavy ones you have may not be enough."

The next day another woman was ill with labor pains, though according to her, it was too soon. So Anza kept them there another night, while the rains continued.

"Is it always going to rain?" Tomasa asked her mother.

Again the children had been confined a good deal in the tents. Once Feliciana let Tomasa and Eustaquía scoot through the rain to see Gertrudis and the kittens. She hoped this would relieve the boredom for a short time.

The sputtering fires with their eye-smarting smoke annoyed everyone, and tempers sometimes flared. However, Anza didn't want to hurry the sick woman.

Some of the cattle became ill. Apparently the lake was alkaline, and the surrounding plants contained too much salt. Feliciana and a few others were complaining of the taste of the water. She was grateful when she saw Anza sending soldiers, including Muños, for fresh water from the Gila.

67

Finally Anza decided he could wait no longer. Although the woman was still ailing, he had decided to take a short-cut back to the curving Gila before there was more illness. While the soldiers were gone, Anza moved the expedition to better grass a short distance away. The soldiers met them with some fresh water, and Muños had brought extra for Feliciana.

"Give a little to your horse too," Muños cautioned.

"How thoughtful of you," exclaimed Feliciana. "My mouth is dry from that horrid water, and the girls won't drink it at all. Thank you, we really appreciate you looking out for us." She realized he was doing little extra nice things for her to regain her goodwill.

The cattle arrived the day after the camp by the Gila was established. They arrived much weakened by the salt pasturage and bad water.

That day, too, the young woman's baby was born dead. Sadly Feliciana watched as they buried the little one, born too soon due to the rigors of travel.

The rain continued as others became ill, including *Padre* Font. Feliciana put the heavy blankets over her girls and herself when they continued through the rain. She recalled Muños's warning of much rain beyond the rivers, and wondered if this was just the beginning.

But then she brightened as she remembered they would soon meet the chief of the Yuma Indians, about whom Anza had told such colorful tales.

CHAPTER 14

Relief came on Saturday. After a one and a half league march the rain stopped and they arrived at a place the Indians had set up for them previously, not knowing they would be delayed by illness. The Yumas had built bowers of branches such as they used in bad weather.

Under these canopies, laced over and over with branches, the families tried to dry out. But Anza hurried them on the next day. There was no rain, and in four leagues they were again beside the Gila among the waiting Yumas.

Padre Font had them up early for mass. Feliciana thought he still looked ill. He insisted mass must be said before the crossing of the river. By 8:15 Anza and the Yumas had decided on the spot for the first crossing.

From their seats on Gallardo, Eustaquía and Tomasa looked down at the water. It was a shallow place, and the current was slow, but it looked frightening to the children, who had only seen nearly-dry rivers in their own land.

José Pico splashed alongside of them on his horse and laughed at their worried faces.

"Look!" he shouted, "My horse loves it, his feet like it, and I like it! Come on, follow me!"

Feliciana thought it must have felt good to Gallardo too, for he splashed along behind José without hesitation. It took the colonists only a short time to reach the other side.

Muños came and told Feliciana to follow him. He led her and the others up the banks and a short way to a series of hot springs. The women could hardly believe their eyes. Camp was made quickly. Though the air was cold, they lost no time plunging their dirty clothes into the warm waters. Feliciana started them to singing as they worked. Soon clothes were stretched across the bushes and even from the branches of nearby willow trees.

The sun was shining but there was little warmth in it. Feliciana's clothes dried slowly and the heavier ones not at all. It was like old times at home she thought, washing in warm water and singing together.

Anza decided to stay overnight, for the pasturage was good. It was bitter cold in the tent and the girls and Feliciana huddled under all their blankets. In the morning the wood was so cold it took *Señor* Pico a long time starting the breakfast fires.

The heavy clothes, still wet, had been left outside. When Feliciana went to hang hers by the fire, she found them frozen stiff. Everyone felt them wonderingly. How could this be?

Señor Muños came by. "Put some water in a small pan tonight, Tomasa. You will have ice on it tomorrow."

Feliciana watched as the children gathered around Tomasa's pan the next day. She broke the surface with a stick and picked up a piece in her bare hand.

"It burns!" she cried. José took a piece and passed it quickly from one hand to the other. Dolores took another. Feliciana was as fascinated as the children from the warm lands.

José licked a piece and yelled, "It's cold water!"

"Come children, we're ready to move on," called Feliciana. An icy wind was blowing. Huddled in ponchos and blankets, they trudged wearily across a short cut back to another part of the curving Gila River. Again the crossing was easy and the new camp made.

Shortly after they were settled, Feliciana learned a baby boy was born to the wife of a soldier, Ignacio Gutiérrez. The next few days were spent here, as the new mother was in pain and *Padre* Font had a return of his malaria-like illness.

"How long is it going to take to reach California at this rate?" Feliciana asked Jacinta.

Though the weather was milder here by the river, several of the pack animals died, weakened by the salt pasturage and the intense cold that had followed.

Feliciana searched in the saddle bags for the warmest clothes she could find for the girls. The children were growing accustomed to the cold now, but she understood it would grow even colder soon.

When they traveled again, it was along the sandy bottom lands and among little sand hills—*medanos*—covering only five leagues in five hours.

"What's the matter with Gallardo?" asked Tomasa. Twice the sturdy horse had stumbled, almost to his knees one time.

"It's the sand he's walking in," said her mother. Feliciana had noticed the other horses had trouble walking in the deep sand. She didn't let Tomasa know how much this troubled her. He had stood up so well, he just mustn't be crippled now. At night the boys and men cared for all the horses with concern, giving them rubdowns and plenty of feed and water, for the colonists' own lives depended on these animals.

Fortunately the soldiers had brought fresh water for the horses when the other animals had drunk at the salty pond. But this sand was hard on both the horses and cattle. What could happen next, Feliciana wondered.

She felt relieved when they came to good pasturage and camp was made. But in the morning, as they were ready to start again, the men driving the cattle reported to Anza that many of their animals were missing. Anza called a meeting.

Feliciana and Jacinta sat waiting as *Señor* Pico gathered with the other men to hear the news. When he returned he announced, "We are staying here for awhile. The cattle have hidden in the brush and refuse to be driven out. One even attacked the man pulling it. Anza has asked all the men to help."

"Can we come too?" asked Dolores and José together.

"Yes, if you will be careful," their father cautioned.

All day the camp waited for the men and cattle. At about dusk, the boys came panting to the tent, which the women had re-erected, and announced that the cattle were coming.

"They locked their horns in the brush and refused anything we offered them to eat," said Dolores. "It was like they were saying they had had enough traveling."

Since the men and cattle were exhausted, the group remained still another day. The rest helped the horses too. Gallardo walked more easily, Feliciana noted thankfully. Though the way led through more sand hills, Anza stopped them early where there was good feed and water.

During supper an Indian appeared. This time no one was startled. These were Yumas in the little villages now, and all were friendly. After a short conference with Anza and *Padre* Garcés, the native trotted back the way he had come.

"How much longer is it to the Colorado River?" asked Feliciana as Anza came by that evening. "These sandy hills are hard on the horses."

"It will take about two more days I think," Anza answered her. "Unfortunately we must continue through this sandy area. We will take it slowly to save the horses. You have all been so helpful, seldom complaining, even when I know you are miserable. I think you will enjoy seeing this Yuma chief, whom we call Salvador Palma. He has embraced our religion and is an intelligent and understanding leader. Good night to you all," and Anza went on to the next group.

CHAPTER 15

On the afternoon of November 27, Palma and thirty or so unarmed Yumas approached the colonists. Greetings were exchanged, with the natives presenting gifts of grain, wheat, calabashes, vegetables and muskmelons.

After camp was made everyone gathered to watch this important chief. *Padre* Garcés acted as interpreter.

Palma spoke first to Anza and the leaders. He stood tall and dignified, and with a definite authoritative manner. Palma spoke passionately. Feliciana thought he looked as though he was praising Anza, whom he had warmly embraced on meeting. The *capitán* had told her he had met the Indian chief when he made his first trip to California.

Then the character of his speech changed. It was as though he was pleading with Anza. Garcés turned to interpret. Feliciana could not hear what he was saying, but heard Anza give his reply.

He thanked the chief for the warm reception of him and all his people. He said they appreciated the gifts, for they had been many days traveling with no fresh food. Then Anza's voice also changed in tone. He said what the chief was asking was impossible. Their great king of Spain had ordered these people to go to California, the new land on the great water. He was sorry they could not stay here and become part of Palma's people. Perhaps someday he would return and start a *pueblo* and mission here, but not on this trip.

Feliciana thought Anza marvelous in his handling of this ticklish situation.

As Garcés translated, she and the others watched anxiously for Palma's reaction. Anza had told them that the crossing of the Colorado depended on the Yumas and their help. But the chief answered cheerfully and even smiled.

Next Anza asked him about where to cross the river. Would the Yumas help them as before, swimming alongside to steady the horses and guide them ashore?

Feliciana recoiled at his reaction. They all saw him shake his head and wave his arms. Obviously he had said no. A new parley came between Garcés and Palma. There was tension in the air. At last Garcés turned to his leader.

"The chief says the waters are too cold for his men to swim at this time. I asked him about making rafts, but he said the water was too turbulent. The rafts could not be guided, and the water would come through. I asked him if there was any other place than where we crossed before, but he said not at this time." Garcés paused and then continued: "I think his answer to the last is not entirely honest. He wants us to stay here and apparently does not intend to help. I'm sure the water *is* too cold, but I am also sure there is an easier place to cross. I would suggest you accept his answer and present him his gifts at this time."

Anza smiled broadly at Chief Palma to show no hard feelings. He ordered one of his men to bring a chest forward.

Even though there were fires in front of each tent, the colonists huddled closer and closer under their blankets. Feliciana wondered how the Yumas could stand the cold with so little on.

Tomasa spoke to her mother. "What is that Indian doing with that lighted stick?" She pointed to one of the natives in the rear. They watched him pass the burning stick up and down in front of his body. Then he repeated the gesture along his back.

"Why, I think he is warming himself," Feliciana said. They noticed other natives doing the same. What a way to keep warm, she thought.

Anza's man returned and set a chest in front of the *capitán*. Opening it, Anza took out various medals which he presented to the chief's head men. Others received staves as symbols of their positions. Feliciana watched

74

with interest when Anza brought Palma to the chest and took out a Spanish uniform similar to his own.

As he placed each article on the chief's arm, Palma's smile grew broader and broader. Together they went to Anza's tent when the chief showed interest in putting on his new clothes.

A buzz of excitement moved through the watching colonists. Feliciana wondered what Palma would look like. In a short time he stepped out in his Spanish uniform. Over the white linen shirt and knee breeches that laced to the thigh he wore a bright red jacket with gold buttons. The official blue cape, decorated with gold braid, swung jauntily from his broad shoulders, making him a symbol of Spanish power and glory. Atop the Yuma's mounded hair was a hat with a white cockade. Feliciana almost giggled. Palma strutted back and forth so that all might see him, the gold buttons and braid glowing in the firelight. A painted Indian chief in the clothes of a Spanish captain.

The colonists clapped and cheered. At least Anza was restored to Palma's good standing—if ever he had lost it.

Feliciana heard murmurs among her friends about how smart their *capitán* and Garcés were. Perhaps they would yet find a way around this cocky chief.

They had only a short ride the next morning to reach the final crossing of the Gila just above the joining with the Colorado. This was an easy place to ford to where the main village of the Yumas was located.

While the colonists set up their tents, Feliciana saw Anza, Garcés and Font being shown into a special lodge Palma had built for them. The villagers distributed to the Spanish more grain and vegetables, as well as about 3000 watermelons.

Several of the boys roaming around the village noticed Lieutenant Moraga riding out of camp. Since he usually did the scouting, rumors flew wildly. Could he be looking for a place to cross that Palma didn't know about? Impossible. The chief knew his territory well. Feliciana saw Moraga return about supper time, looking very satisfied. He headed directly for Anza's lodge.

That evening the Yumas held a large feast for the travelers. Feliciana enjoyed it, but saw *Padre* Font stick to his own food, brought especially for him. Indian food was dirty, he once had said.

Palma wore his new uniform and again asked Anza to stay. This time Anza replied that, when he returned from California, he would take Palma with him to Mexico City to see the great Spanish headquarters.

There was much coming and going that night. Feliciana was restless and heard voices and horses' footsteps. She knew they were now out of the Apaches' range, but something was going on she didn't understand. The cattle too were restless; she could hear them in the distance, where the guarding cowboys sang to them softly. Gallardo was uneasy also—probably from the unusual Indian village smells, was her guess.

How long would they have to stay here if the Indian chief said it was too cold to cross? She had no urge to ride across a swiftly flowing river, even on Gallardo, who was ordinarily an excellent swimmer. But these days he was worn out from the long stretches with little water, followed by the sandy hills and river bed.

She concentrated on the sunny land of California their leader had promised. He had been there and seen it. He would take them there too, she reassured herself, and slipped into a fitful sleep.

Feliciana and the girls ventured aways into the Indian village the next day. The women were shy but friendly, especially towards the girls. They were similar to the men in size, but Feliciana was relieved to see that most wore a little skirt made of the inside bark of the willow and cottonwood trees. This was divided into two parts, a shorter one in front. Some had even woven a fabric from the bark strips.

It was Eustaquía who spotted a woman with a rabbit fur tied on as a skirt.

"Soft, *Mamá*, soft," she said, lightly touching the garment.

"No, Eustaquía, no touch." Feliciana pulled the child back to her. But the Indian mother only smiled at the girls. Then she patted Eustaquía's rough-blanket *poncho* and giggled. Feliciana wondered if she should offer the blanket to the woman, but decided that if she did, other Indians might want more and more.

Going back to their tent, Tomasa said, "Do you suppose she was a rich lady to have fur? I'd want it all over me, my arms and top, not just around my middle. How can she be warm?"

"Probably she isn't," said her mother. "These Indians have never known any other way to live. Maybe it's better to not need so much warmth as we do."

Jacinta and Feliciana used much of the food the Yumas had brought, making fresh *tortillas* from the meal. When the expedition started there was supposed to be ample supplies for the entire trip. But the forced stops due to illness and hunting lost cattle had exhausted much of this. The pack loads of bushels of flour for *tortillas* and corn meal for *pinole* were dangerously low.

Each family had received several of the watermelons. By supper Tomasa moaned, "More watermelon? Do we have to eat watermelon at every meal?"

"Yes," said her mother. "You need all the water you can get, even if it is from watermelons."

All day the men and older boys had been missing. *Señora* Pico could only speculate, "Perhaps they have gone to help Anza find a better way to cross the river. But Santiago would never know if it was good or not. He knows nothing of such waters as this one."

Feliciana just nodded her head. She too had never seen such a swiftly-flowing river.

By supper all had returned. Afterwards Anza, the two *padres* and Moraga joined the people around the fires. Later the two Pico boys joined their family, chuckling.

"*Padre* Font is very unhappy," Dolores said. "He is angry at the *capitán* for giving the military clothes to Chief Palma. He says that honor should have been his, for he is the spiritual leader."

"What did Anza say to that?" asked his father.

"He said he was surprised a *padre* would give military things to anyone. And besides, this was not sent by the Pope but by the King of Spain. *Padre* Font just grumbled and walked away. He can never get the best of our *Capitán* Anza. I suppose we will get an extra mass tomorrow for the 'souls of the great lords.' "

Feliciana gasped at Dolores expressing a judgment on a *padre* out loud, though she had to admit she had also had occasion to do so—but to herself.

"Careful *niño*, he is a good man, but he doesn't look at things as a military man would," said his father. "Besides, he is ill a good deal of the time. And speaking of ill, how is *Padre* Garcés? I heard he is not well."

"*Padre* Garcés never speaks of his illness. I'm sorry that he is to leave us here. He is fun to have around."

"I heard he is going to explore the areas around here before moving on," said his father. "He is a brave man. He travels among the Indians alone, or sometimes with only an Indian helper."

Being a man perhaps helped, but Feliciana had no desire to travel these lands alone, even if the natives were friendly.

Pico went on, laughing a little. "I've heard that *Padre* Font is sure Garcés is part Indian. He eats with them, sitting on the ground, and stays there for hours talking with them. He knows practically all the dialects around here. Well, I wonder what Anza's plans are for us tomorrow."

Feliciana echoed this. She did hope they could get moving again, remembering Muños' warning of perhaps bad weather ahead.

CHAPTER 16

Before he returned to the lodge, Anza spoke to the people. "Tomorrow we are to leave early. I have found a place where I think it will be safe to cross. The river divides into three parts with sand bars between, so the force of the river is broken. We will readjust the loads on the animals when we get there—it is only about a quarter of a league away."

By seven, the morning of November 30, they were on the march again—a short one, as Anza had said. They stood on a high ridge looking down on the water. It was the roughest and fastest any of the colonists had ever seen. True, the two land spits divided the river into three parts, making the crossing about six hundred feet wide, but not deep.

The packers and soldiers came to each family. Saddle bags and all excess baggage were removed. These would be collected after the families were safely across.

Francisco Muños stopped beside Feliciana. "I will stay near you. In fact, I suggest I take one of the girls with me. It will be easier for you to hold only one. How about it, Tomasa?"

The latter gave her mother a stricken look and clutched her tighter.

"Thank you, *Señor* Muños, I think you're right. Now, Tomasa, it will be easier for both of us. If I'm holding Eustaquía, I can't help you much. Be a good girl and slide down and go with *Señor* Muños."

Tomasa made no further objection. Muños helped her into the saddle in front of him, explaining he could hold her better in case his horse balked a little.

Cautiously the group crept down the rough narrow trail to the river's edge. As they waited their turn at the bottom, Muños said to Feliciana, "Many of the older boys and men spent yesterday and last night cutting this road from the ridgetop down to the river. I think Chief Palma knew about this place but wanted us to stay with him, at least through the winter."

So that's where the men and boys were—and the un-usual sounds she had heard in the night, Feliciana thought. Anxiously she watched as the first horses stepped into the swirling waters. It was not deep, but the waves splashed high, sending water even up to the horses' shoulders and onto the riders at times.

"Look at *Padre* Garcés," called Tomasa, giggling. Feliciana had to laugh too.

Three of Anza's Indian guides had picked up the genial *padre*. He stiffened himself while one held up his legs and the other two lifted him at the shoulders. Holding him high, they stepped into the water and carried him safely to the far side. He thanked them and waved back to the colonists.

"Those Indians must be mighty cold," said Feliciana, "but they really love *Padre* Garcés. I wonder how *Padre* Font is going to cross?"

Ten soldiers had stationed themselves across the lower side of the river. If anyone or any baggage should fall, they were there to rescue it.

Now it was the turn of Muños and Tomasa. Muños stepped out boldly, saying, "This is nothing. Don't be afraid, Tomasa, my horse is steady and not afraid of water."

Feliciana came close behind them. As they crossed the second bar she began to relax. Almost across. Gallardo had ventured out timidly at first, but now was steady, even with the water splashing them at times. Feliciana knew her skirt was wet, but Eustaquía was dry and laughing at all the noise around them.

As Muños and Tomasa started into the third section, he turned to wave at Feliciana. A wave suddenly jolted the horse, causing Muños's left knee to slap sharply against the animal. Startled, it reared slightly, but enough for the onrushing water to knock it from its feet. Tomasa cried out as she was thrown into the river while Muños struggled to hold onto the horse.

Feliciana watched helplessly as the small body was tumbled over and over. But the men downstream were waiting and one of them snatched Tomasa as she swept by. Others caught the horse and held it as an abashed Muños struggled to his feet.

Feliciana never remembered how she reached the other side. She was off Gallardo in a flash, dumping Eustaquía into someone's arms. She rushed to meet the man with Tomasa. Frantically she hugged the child and wiped her face. Together they collapsed on the sandy beach, Tomasa clutching her mother and crying hysterically.

"Gracias, gracias, Madre de Dios!" Feliciana murmured over and over. *"Gracias."*

Someone took Tomasa's wet clothes off and wrapped her in a dry blanket. Most of the rest had crossed before Feliciana quit shaking.

A subdued Muños apologized over and over again to Feliciana. Tomasa would have nothing to do with him. Eustaquía was returned to her mother and the three sat huddled together while the animals returned to the far side, were reloaded, and made the trip back safely.

Feliciana had been shaken by the near tragedy, but her mood changed to amusement as she watched *Padre* Font. He had insisted that he would ride, but because he was ill he wanted Indians supporting him on each side. He had refused to let his baggage be removed. When he dismounted after the crossing, he was angered to find his saddle bags containing his vestments were soaked.

Camp was made high on the bank. Wet clothes were set to dry near the fires. Anza went among the people congratulating them on their courage, checking on those who were ill, and telling them they would stay here a few days to recover.

To Feliciana he said, "Relax. That was the last large river to cross."

A shout came from the far side—and there was Palma.

"I wonder if he is angry because we found a place to cross," Dolores Pico said. "Palma thought it was too cold for swimming, but our Indian guides weren't afraid." He and some of the other boys watched as the chief descended to the river and crossed it, walking through the water.

The chief was smiling though, as he came up the bank to Anza and began a conference with the Spanish leader.

With the others, Feliciana had the feeling that Chief Palma had merely tried to keep them there. Perhaps it would have added to his esteem among the other tribes if he had a Spanish *pueblo* and mission near his people.

"So we are to stay here for a few days," *Señora* Pico said. "Well, a good time to rearrange our clothes for the cold weather ahead. We can dry everything—if it doesn't rain," she added anxiously, looking at the gray sky.

"I hear Chief Palma is building a cabin for *Padre* Garcés to stay in," *Señor* Pico said. "Anza asked some of us to help."

"Is he going to stay here long?" asked Feliciana.

"Only until he is well again. Apparently he was ill during the talks with Palma, but Garcés didn't tell anyone. He's not like *Padre* Font. I'll admit Font seldom gives in to his ailments, but he enjoys them out loud and makes everyone near him suffer too."

"I'm sorry *Padre* Garcés is leaving us," Feliciana said. All agreed with her, and wondered if they would ever see the jolly little *padre* again.

Three days later when Anza moved them on to better pasturage about half an hour's walk away, Chief Palma waved them on their way. He assured Anza he would care for the *padre* and the men left with him. Anza was also leaving some of the horses and cattle that were too weak to travel. He would pick them up on his return trip.

COLORADO RIVER
TO SAN GABRIEL

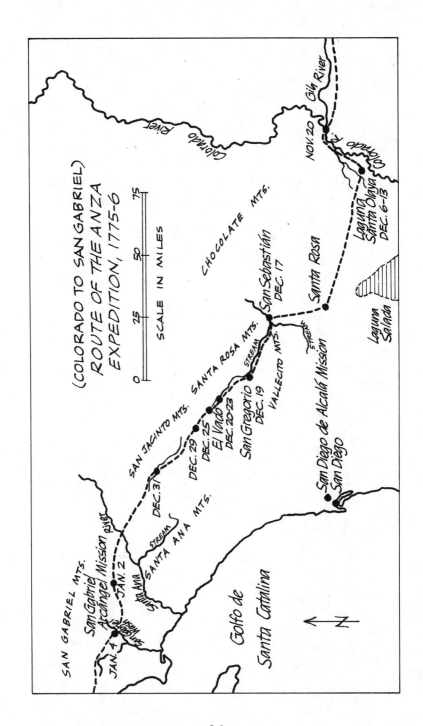

(COLORADO TO SAN GABRIEL)
ROUTE OF THE ANZA
EXPEDITION, 1775-6

SCALE IN MILES

0   25   50   75

Colorado River

Gila River

NOV. 20

Laguna
Santa Olaya
DEC. 6-13

CHOCOLATE MTS.

San Sebastián
DEC. 17

Santa Rosa

Laguna
Salada

SAN JACINTO MTS.   SANTA ROSA MTS.

VALLECITO MTS.

STREAM

DEC. 31

DEC. 29

El Vado
DEC. 25

San Gregorio
DEC. 20-23
DEC. 19

San Diego de Alcalá Mission
San Diego

STREAM

SANTA ANA MTS.

SANTA ANA

SAN GABRIEL MTS.
San Gabriel
Arcángel Mission River
JAN. 2

JAN. 4

Golfo de
Santa Catalina

N

84

CHAPTER 17

Monday, December 4, 1775, saw the start of the final part of the journey. Anza warned them the night before of some of the difficulties they might meet. He praised them for their willingness to endure for the sake of the wonderful new land just ahead—though Feliciana hoped there wasn't too much more to endure.

Instead of heading north and west, Anza chose to take the expedition south first, and travel around the great desert that was just to the north.

The 3000 watermelons given them had been distributed long ago. Feliciana and the girls agreed with the others they had consumed all the watermelons they could possibly eat. Many had to be left behind because of the weight.

Their travel led through small Indian villages where the natives were shy but friendly. However, they slowed down the expedition because of their curiosity. They touched blankets wonderingly, and gazed at the people and horses in amazement. Feliciana shrank from close contact, her near abduction still fresh in her mind, even though the Yuma Indians had been friendly.

Camp was made at the end of five leagues. Some cattle were still behind, caught in the brush and thickets.

It seemed to Feliciana that the cold was more intense that night. Would they ever be warm again? Many needed Anza's medication, and several saddle animals died because of the extreme cold and exhaustion.

They traveled only three leagues the next day, waiting for the cattle to catch up. Fortunately there was plenty of wood, and boys were sent collecting it as soon as they stopped. With blankets at their backs and roaring fires in front, Tomasa and Eustaquía snuggled close to their mother as they ate their supper that night. Feliciana thought of the days to come. How many more must they endure?

"I wonder if I will ever be warm again," murmured *Doña* Jacinta. Her girls were so wrapped in blankets they looked like little roly-poly bears. "How do these Indians survive?"

"We saw some of them rolled in balls by their fires," said José. "They just burrowed down into the dust like animals."

"Ugh!" said Tomasa. "Why do they stay here?"

"They don't travel far unless something drives them away," answered her mother. "And I guess they have good weather in the summertime when all those watermelons are growing. It's their home, too."

All were quiet, thinking of the homes left behind, Feliciana guessed.

Dolores spoke first. "I'm glad we came, though. Sometimes it's miserable, but think of all the new good foods we have had."

José spoke up, "Then we had a shock, seeing the Yumas the first time; and then Chief Palma all dressed up. He's kind of like a child—wanting to show off and having so many people to rule."

"Well, I didn't like falling off the horse," Tomasa exclaimed.

"But think what you can tell your grandchildren about," teased José. "You were the only one, and you survived. You and that Muños."

Feliciana had private thoughts about Muños. He was attractive when he smiled, but like a spoiled child when he was crossed. He had been more than kind since the river accident, but neither girl liked him. Sometimes she thought he was too bossy, but then most men were, she noticed. He had let the other men know he wanted her, and this displeased her greatly.

Four leagues further took them to a place called Laguna Santa Olaya. This was the territory of the Cajuenches, closely related to the Yumas. Scarcely had camp been made than several friendly natives arrived with about a thousand fish, an hour's catch, from the little lake.

Cries of joy greeted Anza as he and his men distributed the gifts. Feliciana happily cleaned the little fish—a welcome change in their diet. Their early supper was interrupted by the arrival of *Padre* Garcés.

"*Padre! Padre!*" called out the campers. "You look wonderful. We're so glad to see you."

He waved them back to their suppers, saying, "I will talk to you later. Don't stop now."

"He made a fast recovery," Feliciana commented. "Chief Palma took good care of him. I think he is stronger than *Padre* Font too." All agreed.

Cheers greeted Garcés when he came out of Anza's tent. He said he was so near he decided to spend the night with them and then go on down the Colorado River to visit the tribe at the mouth.

On his way back to Anza's tent, *Padre* Garcés asked Feliciana if he might speak with her.

"Of course," she replied, puzzled as to why he had singled her out.

Leading her away from the others, he reached inside his robe and brought out a small leather-wrapped packet. This he placed in Feliciana's hands. Wonderingly she opened the gift and gave a small cry of pleasure. It was the good luck blue stone Juana had given her.

Garcés explained, "An Indian runner gave this to me in Palma's camp. He asked me to find you or send it on."

"But why?" asked Feliciana. "I gave it to them. It was to bring them good luck."

"Their medicine man told them the charm would bring good luck to you only. Since the 'Good Luck *Señora*' had used the charm to buy her freedom, it would have no powers for them."

Garcés went on. "The runner said a little magic must have rubbed off on them, for later some hunters brought back a few rabbits for supper. They still think you are the 'Good Luck *Señora*,' even though the medicine man made them send it back. Now they hope the luck is still in the stone. The tribes all believe there will be unusually bad weather in the next few weeks, and say you will surely need the good luck stone."

Feliciana ran her hand over the freshly cleaned thong and glanced at Garcés.

"Yes," he answered her unspoken question. "It was greasy when I received it. By cleaning it perhaps my wishes will double the power of the turquoise charm."

"*Padre* Garcés, you know I don't really believe in charms such as this. But it is special to me because of the one who gave me it. She lived in dire poverty, with this her only treasure. And she gave it to me." There were tears in Feliciana's eyes as she slipped the thong around her neck.

"Thank you, *Padre* Garcés, for going out of your way to bring it to me. Please pray for us that the Indian's predictions are wrong, and if not, that the charm will still be working."

Back in the group, Feliciana could only shudder with the others and shake her head. To start out in this weather with only two Indians was more than they could understand. They cheered him and asked his blessing on their journey.

Anza joined them then at the campfires, which these days were as close to the tents as possible. "We come now to a difficult part of our expediton. Again it is because of the shortage of water. For the next three days I am dividing you into three sections. I will lead the first with *Padre* Font. *Sargente* Grijalva will follow with the second, and Lieutenant Moraga will bring the third."

Feliciana's spirits fell. They were to be separated. She trusted Anza, but this would be a terrible area to be lost in.

Anza went on: "The first and second groups will water their saddle horses and stock before dawn at the first two stops. In that way there should be water by the time the next caravan arrives. We will wait at San Sebastián to be reunited."

Feliciana was glad when Anza said, "Tomorrow we will rest. There are several people ill. This will give them more time to recover and the rest of us to be prepared. This is good pasturage, so let your livestock eat and rest."

One last chance to be all together—Feliciana had a sudden foreboding, unusual for her.

"And finally, let's celebrate a little. Tomorrow we'll have a *fandango*—brandy and all."

There were cheers and shouts from the people. *Padre* Font stalked back to his tent. Not even his shaking with the ague prevented him from walking stiffly and erect, showing his anger like a bantam rooster, Feliciana thought irreverently.

The Picos and Feliciana were put in the first group along with some of those still sick. They would have another day of rest at the end, waiting for the second and third groups. Feliciana wasn't sure staying in this cold place was a pleasure, but at least there was water and food. She was pleased to find Muños was not in her group. He was becoming more and more irritable when she spent time with others.

As promised, the brandy keg was unloaded the next day. There would be no fancy dressing for this dance. At first the musicians grumbled at the cold, but their love of music was too strong.

When she sang some of the more popular ones, the men cheered and joined her. She was overwhelmed with partners as the dancing started. She pretended she didn't see Muños, and danced first with one and then another. At last he claimed his turn, and Feliciana smiled coquettishly at him. She was glad he saw he was not the only man ready to aid her, although she knew it made him angry.

There was no wild *fandango* as at Tubac, thus avoiding any trouble with Muños or Font.

There were cries of "Dance, *Doña* Feliciana, dance," but she ignored them and stayed with Muños until another broke in. Muños sulked on the side. He danced with no other and kept his eyes on Feliciana. His cup of brandy was never empty for long, and she could see him grow angrier and angrier.

Finally he could stand it no longer. He strode into the group of dancers, grabbed Feliciana by the arm and dragged her beyond the tents.

Padre Font, eyes gleaming with approval, followed at a distance. He had told Anza in the beginning that the widow spelled trouble. Muños grabbed her shoulders and repeatedly shook her.

"You have no business dancing with all those other men. I forbid it, you hear me?"

Feliciana shrank from his drunken anger. "You have no right to tell me what to do."

"I have every right. You should have a good beating until you are a proper wife."

Feliciana gasped. "I have never said I would be your wife, and I never will be. My husband never treated me so." She tried to pull away, and at last freed one hand and slapped him sharply.

Startled, Muños let her go and she returned quickly to the safety of the group. She saw him stagger away. What next, she wondered.

With the two little ones huddled close to her, Feliciana was too angry to sleep. What right had he to tell her what to do? Had she been too friendly of late? She had forgiven him his letting Tomasa fall into the river. He was not used to remembering that children came first, and then you save yourself. He had been so contrite ever since and had done his best to win back Tomasa's good will. But now both girls disliked him, although they were friendly with other soldiers who helped them. Thankfully she remembered he was not in the first group, and so she would be free of him for a few days.

Padre Font aroused them for an early mass. He scolded all for their levity and drunkenness and noise of the night before. He named no names this time, but Feliciana could feel him looking at her.

She tossed her head. It was not of her doing, that quarrel with Muños, though perhaps she had flirted a bit too much. She saw Font draw Anza aside with much gesticulating, and guessed he was scolding their leader for having given the people brandy. Anza shrugged the *padre* off and went about organizing the first group—too much else on his mind, Feliciana guessed.

CHAPTER 18

The next days become a nightmare in Feliciana's memory. The journey from Laguna de Santa Olaya, where Garcés left, to San Sebastián, three days later, was a blur. Strong icy winds, dark threatening clouds, and the spattering of rain turning to a blizzard was the setting.

There were wells that had to be opened over and over to provide a trickling of water for the pack and saddle animals. Families carried their own supplies. The cattle were being driven straight through without food or water. Feliciana wondered how they would make it.

The cold that followed was so penetrating that even the largest and hottest fires warmed only the surface. She fingered the icy charm and slipped it down inside her clothes, hoping it could somehow warm the three of them. Feliciana remembered making mittens for the girls and herself from an end of her blanket, and rolling the three of them together in it at night for warmth, with the rest of their perpetually damp blankets over them.

Only on the second night was there plenty of firewood. Anza urged them to carry some along the next day, for there would be only a small amount at the third stop, San Sebastián. He said they must make that do until all arrived and they could move on.

But the blizzard at San Sebastián froze all memory for awhile. Winds hurled the snow in every direction. Many horses and pack animals died of exhaustion after having followed Anza and Font blindly into the teeth of the storm.

Feliciana did remember giving Gallardo the last of his

rations and keeping him tethered close to the tent for shelter. Without him she feared they would never get out of this world of snow and cold.

After reinforcing their tents and eating cold food to save the firewood, she had sunk into a numb state of waiting for the other two groups.

The arrival of some of the cattle cheered them all a bit. They killed a dying animal and soon the stew kettles were bubbling over meager fires. Many of the cattle died on the way, with the survivors searching frantically for food.

She knew when the second group under Sergeant Grijalva finally straggled in, with three men near death. The first group aroused themselves and wrapped blankets around the men and put them between the fires. Feliciana knew these were the men—soldiers and packers—who had no tents and were forced to huddle under whatever brush they could find.

Then time lost meaning, not only for Feliciana but for all. Was it one or three days they stayed in this frozen area waiting for Moraga's group? She couldn't remember. Only later, counting back from Christmas, did she decide it was four days until Anza sent two men and twenty horses to look for them.

Through this darkness of mind and spirit shone a shaft of light. It was Anza, consoling, cheering, wiping tears from little faces, and reminding them all that the good land really was just a little way ahead. But even Anza's face was etched with fatigue and worry by the time he sent the two men to hunt for Moraga. Again Feliciana had that haunting feeling that something had gone wrong. Her hand reached for the charm.

Were they lost in the blizzard and frozen to death? Were one third of their party—by now like brothers and sisters—lost? Feliciana, like the rest, sat in a gray world of waiting.

When all hope seemed running out, a shout went up. Out of the mists came first a few shapes and then more and more. The grayness of mind vanished as members of the third group straggled in on the relief horses Anza had sent.

Nearly frozen, they could only murmur that the rest were indeed coming. Near the end of that afternoon, bringing up the rear of the people, mules and even some cattle, came Moraga. Feliciana felt a great uplift—the foreboding was gone.

A mighty cheer rose up for this popular man, second to Anza. He haltingly explained the blizzard had caught them in an unprotected spot with no pasturage or water. Most of his animals had died.

A large *mantilla* was wrapped around his head. A spasm of pain crossed his face as he removed it. Anza rushed him into his tent when Moraga said his ears pained him frightfully.

Fires were heaped high with the hoarded firewood, and new ones started. The men in camp set up the tents of the new arrivals. Feliciana helped Jacinta prepare and serve hot drinks. Two exhausted beeves had been slaughtered earlier and, with beans and *tortillas,* provided a feast for the reunited colonists.

The next morning was spent salting the meat of cattle just dead. It was not very appetizing—the meat was poor color and smelly—but it was food. Then Anza led them to a better pasturage in a meadow about three and a half leagues away. Here was plenty of firewood, and even the sun shone, although they were soon again surrounded by storm clouds.

To celebrate their joy at being reunited, Anza brought out a brandy keg, and those unbeatable people swung from despair to rejoicing, calling for a *fiesta.*

Again there were no fancy clothes, but cries of "*Fandango, fandango*" turned the dance that night into a laughing, noisy and emotional celebration.

"Sing, *Doña* Feliciana," came the cries. So she sang, many of them the favorites of the men.

In the dance that followed, Feliciana was again in great demand as a partner. No one noticed the cold. The musicians outdid themselves, and Feliciana danced with the abandon she had shown that night in Tubac—but not the *fandango.*

Into the center strode Muños, his face dark with anger. He caught Feliciana's arm and pulled her roughly from the group and into a nearby tent.

Anza and Font heard her cry for help and rushed to

where Muños was trying to beat her. When Anza ordered the soldier to stop, *Padre* Font chided him: "She is a bad woman, *Capitán*. She deserves to be beaten."

"If she is to be my wife, she must obey me," Muños defended himself.

"Never!" cried Feliciana. She yanked herself free.

"There will be no drunken brawling," Anza said sternly to Muños. "Get out and leave this young woman alone."

"*Señor*, she has led me on. I have aided her, brought her water. She has acted as though she wished to be my wife, and no woman should dance as she did tonight."

As he reached the tent flap, he turned and said, "If she will obey me, I'm still willing to marry her." Then he drunkenly stomped off.

Feliciana was in tears. "*Capitán* Anza, I am sorry I have caused so much disturbance. But I don't want to marry him. I don't want to marry anyone. I was carried away by such relief and happiness for us all that I forgot myself. I will not dance again on this trip."

"Perhaps it was I who should not have given out the brandy," said Anza. "We are all at a high pitch this night and under great emotional stress. Don't blame yourself, *Doña* Feliciana. Has anyone else annoyed you?"

She shook her head wordlessly. Anza went on, "I shall stop the dancing now. Forget what happened tonight. I understand you very well and I think you will make a wonderful contribution to the new *pueblo*."

Font had no such concerns for the health of the people, Feliciana realized. His concern was with their behavior and souls. He summoned them to an early mass the next morning at which he spoke sharply. He accused them of holding "festivities in honor of the devil."

He wondered why the commander was more worried about the threatened beating of the widow than about the scandal of the dance itself.

Feliciana, drained of all feeling, half-listened to Font. How could she evade Muños from now on? Once it had seemed there might be something between them. But his drunkenness and anger had turned her away from him forever. He would never be the man for her.

CHAPTER 19

Since they were up early, Anza had them on the way by nine o'clock. The new stop was at a place called San Gregorio, a watering place. But the water gave out even before the saddlehorses had finished drinking. Anza ordered more holes opened, but the water flowed slowly. Feliciana watched and worried. Without water no one could live.

The Picos spoke of this that night. "We were fortunate the Indians gave us so many watermelons. We're not in need of water as much as the animals are." One of Santiago Pico's horses had died the night before and the children were upset.

In truth, Feliciana had been tired of watermelons and resented the weight for her horse to carry. Already burdened, many of the horses had also brought firewood from the last camp. But now the colonists were appreciating the gifts of the Indians.

As night came on, Tomasa and Eustaquía clung even closer to their mother. They were colder than they had ever been in their lives. Before going to bed, Feliciana rolled them in her extra blanket, which she had warmed first. She decided to stay out by the fire along with most of the other people.

Few slept on this frigid night. The men took turns bringing more wood to keep the fires blazing. Tears almost froze on the cheeks of some of the women. Feliciana was sure they were thinking the same as she: would this cold ever end, or would they all eventually die, as the animals were?

Three of the colonists' horses did die during the night. Gallardo, once so big and strong, was now only a shadow of his former self. Actually the mounts from the *presidios* at Horcasitas and Tubac were still in fair shape, compared to the others. They had been used to fast marches under all kinds of conditions, Feliciana guessed. Also, the soldiers were used to caring for them first, before they tended to themselves.

She stroked and talked to her horse. "Poor Gallardo. I never thought to treat you like this. Can you hold out a little longer? Without you the girls and I will never make it to California." He whinnied softly, resting his head on her shoulder.

There was no mass in the morning. Word came that Font was ill again and unable to lead the *Alabado* as they started.

They traversed the meadow, about four leagues, and then crossed the small Coyote Creek. From here Feliciana could see that the only way out was up and over the mountains. They stayed in this place three days to allow the cattle that were still on their feet to rest and eat.

As the tents were being set up, Tomasa ran to her mother and said, "Look, some Indians are running away. Do you suppose they have gone to bring more back?"

Feliciana and Tomasa watched as Dolores and José Pico ran to where the natives had disappeared. They returned with a few gourds, blankets of rabbit skins and a bow. There were seeds in some of the gourds, though many had spilled out as they ran.

The boys showed these to Anza, asking, "Can we keep these? They just threw them away."

"I think they were frightened by us. If we keep them, they'll think we are enemies. These seeds are their food. Also the bow is their only weapon, and as for the blankets, how can they keep warm without them? Only enemies take away the means to live. No, boys, put them back where they were dropped, maybe a little further along the trail. When they get courage, perhaps they will return for them."

The boys were disappointed, but Anza said, "Would you like those Indians to take your horse and food? Sometime we might need their help."

The boys looked doubtful at that but returned the lost

96

articles. Perhaps the boys wanted souvenirs, Feliciana thought.

"That was an awful dirty blanket," Dolores told the tent family later. "It was warm, but it sure smelled. And how could that little pinch of seeds feed them? And how could such people feed us?"

The night before they were to go on again it started to rain. Feliciana was utterly discouraged—always rain or snow or wind—and now Christmas coming, too.

Dolores came in to supper to say the Indians had come for their belongings. "And not only did they come back, they stayed and watched us. Then Anza took them some food. I hope we don't starve because he gave away some of ours," he added grumbling. He looked at his meager supper of smelly meat strips in the thin vegetable stew. Feliciana understood his feeling but approved of Anza's way.

His father shushed him. "Anza knows these Indians better than we do. It is better to have friends than enemies here in this wild area." That, too, Feliciana agreed with.

Although it had stopped raining in the morning as they packed up, it soon started again. Feliciana had planned for this next rain. She mounted Gallardo with Eustaquía. *Don* Santiago spread a blanket over the horse's back with the front edge tucked under the saddle. Next he lifted Tomasa onto the blanket and pulled it around the child and over her head.

As the rain now pelted them, Feliciana reached back for the blanket and pulled it over her head and Eustaquía's too, then down and around them all. She left a peephole to see the path. Now the three were covered and held warmly to each other. Tomasa squeezed her mother gratefully.

The horses picked their way among the boulders and then started the upward climb. The way was slippery along the small rocks and pebbles, and Feliciana had to trust Gallardo to find the best way. There were no trees and the bitter wind rushed down the canyon walls, blowing the rain straight at them.

Anza stopped the expedition early and fires were started from the small amount of firewood they had carried. *Padre* Font joined them around the fires, shaking with chills and unhappy with everyone, especially Anza. Feliciana noted the latter ignored the *padre*; it was no time to quarrel with him.

Then, filtering down from the rock-strewn hills, came a procession of Indians. Nervously Eustaquía and Tomasa clung to Feliciana and watched as Anza went to meet them. They gave him small bundles of firewood and a gift of food.

"What do you know!" exclaimed Dolores. "How does Anza do it—get the Indians on his side?"

His father replied rather drily, "And you were the one who didn't want to share your food with those poor creatures."

While the firewood didn't go very far, it was comforting to Feliciana to know they were not alone in a friendless land.

The Peraltas and the Alvisos were huddling around the Picos' fire that night when one of the children said, "Tomorrow will be the day before Christmas—it won't be like home," and burst into tears.

Feliciana had been thinking the same thing, but hadn't wanted to remind the girls of it.

"Would you children like to plan something?" asked *Señora* Peralta. "Perhaps we will stop early tomorrow, and the weather might be better, too."

"Could we? Could we?" came from all sides.

"You stay here with the men by the fire. We mothers have something to talk about also." Feliciana and the women went to join some other women at another fire. It was not a Christmas celebration they were talking about, though. Rather, they were concerned with *Señora* Linares, whose baby was due any time.

"*Doña* Gertrudis says she is not feeling well," said *Doña* Jacinta. "She says she is so tired she can't go another day."

"Does *el Capitán* know?" asked Feliciana.

"Oh yes. *Doña* Gertrudis didn't want to worry him, but I told him," said *Doña* Jacinta. "He is always so concerned for us and he said he would watch her carefully."

"Now, about the children and Christmas. Do any of you still have some brown sugar? We might make *panocha* if we stop early."

"I'll help," Feliciana offered.

"Haven't they been wonderful on this whole trip?" said another. "They have complained really very little. Yes, I have some brown sugar, *Doña* Jacinta. I'd like to help make a treat for them."

Others agreed, and Feliciana and *Doña* Jacinta and their friends went back to see what the children had been thinking.

The latter could hardly wait for the women to sit down. "We are going to have a *Posada!*" they all exclaimed.

"But how? Where can you go? Where are your costumes?"

"Oh, *Mamá*," said nine-year-old Gertrudis. "We don't need costumes. Mary and Joseph just wore the clothes they were traveling in. And we even picked Joseph and Mary," she added triumphantly.

"They picked Luís for Joseph, because he is so tall. And we picked Tomasa because she was the only one who got dumped into the river. And she's pretty, too."

Feliciana thought that a strange combination of reasons, but was happy for Tomasa, who was usually on the quiet side.

Señora Peralta looked embarrassed. "There are other tall boys in the camp beside your brother," she said

"It's all right," said another girl. "Luís was here and he said he'd do it. We had to coax Tomasa, but everyone wanted her. And tomorrow we'll just go round to the other camps and tell the boys and girls to follow Joseph and Mary. They know what to do and Luís even knows the words. All the parents know the words too, we're sure. So we *can* celebrate Christmas. It's all right, isn't it?"

"Of course, José," and *Doña* Jacinta put an arm across her son's shoulders. This trip was helping him to think about other people, she noticed. Feliciana too had observed how dependable José was becoming, and was glad for her friend.

CHAPTER 20

The next morning they traveled through a dense fog until Anza called a halt about noon. They were on a broad shelf above the raging water below. Only a few days ago Feliciana had wondered if they would ever find enough water. Now here was more than they could ever use.

There was no wind under the fog and it was not as cold as before. All kindled their fires and ate the noon meal in silence. Word had come that *Señora* Linares had started into labor.

Afterwards the children scampered from camp to camp enlisting other children for the *Posada,* and the mothers made the brown sugar candy. Talk was low, with many glances towards the tent used for those who were ill.

After supper the children gathered near the Picos' tent. There was much giggling and shushing as they formed the line that would search for lodging for Joseph and Mary. Feliciana and Jacinta sat watching, pleased to see how the children were handling Christmas.

Luís put Tomasa on the Peralta's donkey and led the group to the Castros' tent. He stopped and faced *Señor* Castro, singing:

> In the name of Heaven
>> A lodging for the night.
> She can go no further,
>> My beloved wife.

Señor Castro answered:

We have no lodging for you.
    Begone and on your way.
How do we know who you may be?
    There is no place to stay.

With bowed heads the blanket-robed little Holy Family and their followers trudged on to the next camp. Again Luís sang:

In the name of Heaven
    A lodging for the night.
She can go no further,
    My beloved wife.

This time *Señor* Sanchez answered:

We have no lodging for you.
    Begone and on your way.
How do we know who you may be?
    There is no place to stay.

Feliciana, watching, thought how true it was. They had no home, and who knew where they—all of them—might find one? How far were these children going to travel before they reached their destination?

The group had come full circle. Luís repeated the request to *Señor* Pico, who replied:

We have lodging, though poor and mean,
    That we will share with you.
We cannot turn you out this night,
    Be our guests, please do.

"We have no *piñata* tonight, but maybe these little *dulces* will do." Feliciana smiled, seeing the children's surprise at the platters of *panocha*.

While the children surrounded the women, Anza emerged from the hospital tent. "I thought I heard a *Posada* in progress. Is this your reward?"

"*Sí, Capitán*. Have some of our *panocha*," Luís said, offering his mother's platter to Anza.

"*Señores*, you are wonders. When did you make this? And a most fitting celebration for another event. *Señora* Linares has a fine healthy boy. He is to be named Salvador for our Saviour: Salvador Ignacio Linares. Let's have a *fiesta* tonight to crown this special day. I'm ordering some brandy. First the *Posada* and then the birth of a baby. A real Christmas."

Everyone cheered as he moved away to order the *aguardiente*—that is, all but one. Feliciana saw *Padre* Font follow Anza and heard him accuse the leader in front of all.

"Did I hear '*aguardiente* for all?' "

"You did," answered Anza quietly.

"Well, *Señor*, it does not seem right to me that we celebrate the birth of the Infant Jesus with drunkenness." He stalked off to his tent.

Later, with the appearance of the brandy, there were calls for the musicians. Singing and dancing followed. Feliciana, though she sang some of the songs the soldiers called for, danced little that night. She turned down *Don* Muños with a shake of her head. She wanted no more confrontations with him, especially in front of all. As far as she was concerned, he was out of her life forever.

The storm that had been threatening all day now loomed darkly over them. The tremendous mountains around them were lost in the clouds.

On Christmas morning Font aroused the colonists early. Murky mists surrounded Feliciana as she shepherded the girls to where *Padre* Font was to hold mass. In the penetrating chill he held not only one mass, but three, and required everyone to stay the entire time.

In the first mass he accused them all of the sins of gluttony, wild dancing and drunkenness. He urged them to repentance on that Holy Day. In the second mass he gave thanks that they had come so far with so little loss of life. Also it was a mass for Christmas Day and the Holy Child.

Then, in the third service he baptized the new baby, Salvador Ignacio, son of Ignacio and Gertrudis Linares.

Since the new mother was suffering great pain, they stayed on another day to give her a chance to recover.

Feliciana mused that perhaps Anza too, after the confrontation with Font and three masses, needed a day of rest.

CHAPTER 21

Early the 27th of December Anza gave the order to march. Feliciana commented, "*Señora* Linares is a plucky woman to be willing to be on the way so soon."

"I understand Anza asked her how the baby liked to travel, and she said the baby was ready to go. I guess she wants to get out of this *cañon* and up on top."

"I wonder what is on top? It looks like more mountains in every direction. Is there really a way out?"

The rain that had held off now poured on them as they started the last steep climb. It turned to sleet and again Feliciana had the girls huddle close to her under the still soggy blanket. At least they didn't feel the stinging sleet.

In a twisting, turning single file the expedition slowly wound its way up the path to the top. Sleet now turned to snow and soon blotted out everything.

Anza walked from one end of the caravan to the other. Part of the time he led *Señora* Linares' horse while her husband led the other with their three children on it.

It was not a long climb, but steep. At last Anza halted them on what seemed to be the top of the world.

Feliciana threw back the blanket and the three looked in all directions. Snow-topped mountains were all they could see.

"Will we ever go down and be warm, *Mamá*?" asked Tomasa, near tears. Feliciana, thoroughly depressed, wondered the same thing. "Rub your charm, *Mamá*. Maybe it will help."

Anza gave the signal for camp. As they stepped from their horses the ground beneath them suddenly moved. At first Feliciana thought she was a bit dizzy. Then small rocks and boulders rolled past them and one of the women began screaming:

"The mountain is breaking up! We'll all be killed!"

Seized by panic, many grabbed their children, prepared to run.

Anza's voice boomed over all: "Don't panic! That is an earthquake to welcome you to California! See—you feel nothing now."

Uneasily the unpacking continued, but it had been almost the last straw. All they could see were snow-capped mountains, ridge after ridge. Now the earthquake! What would happen next? Tears froze on their cheeks. Feliciana spoke with *Señoras* Pico and Peralta.

"If we show we are not afraid, perhaps we can comfort the others."

They walked among the other women and, with a pat and a hug, calmed them down. The children, though bewildered, slushed around looking for firewood.

Later Anza explained it would only be a few days and their worst problems would be over. No one would believe him when he said spring was just a little way below them.

In fact, when he said this would be a wonderful spot for a *pueblo*, with a wide meadow of grass surrounded by trees, they only saw the snow-covered mountains and wondered who would want to live here.

Anza kept them there another day. The jolting ride had been hard on *Señora* Linares. Feliciana knew she would have wanted more rest under such conditions.

Doña Jacinta had the stewpot over the fire shortly, and Feliciana added dry beans and vegetables. Most of their meat was spoiled, and they left it for the wild animals and birds. However, cattle that died that day were cut up and each campfire added meat to their watery stew. Tough, stringy and with little meat on the bones, it did add flavor, and life looked a little more optimistic.

Fires were kept roaring so that blankets and shawls might dry. No one really believed Anza when he said they would be out of the snow soon. How could they? The snow-topped mountains were everywhere.

Señora Linares said she was well enough the next day to continue. Muffled and covered against the penetrating cold, they were no longer the exuberant group that had set out from Horcasitas three months before. Feliciana and Gallardo were part of an apathetic, stoic column that plodded carefully down the other side of the rock-strewn *cañon*.

Anza had said spring would soon be here. Feliciana wondered how soon was soon? As she held the blanket around the three of them, she wondered if any future was worth this ordeal. It would take a miracle, she was sure— more than any good luck charm could promise. Perhaps she should turn back at San Gabriel. She could wait there for Anza to come back from San Francisco Bay and then return with him to where the sun always shone. That way she could be free of *Señor* Muños. Again he had pestered her to let Tomasa ride with him, saying he could keep her warmer, and that his horse was still in fair condition. He had said this while looking at Gallardo's rib-showing sides.

Tomasa overheard him and shouted "NO!" before ducking quickly behind her mother. Feliciana tried to make amends, but told him she would care for her children herself from here on.

At the start of the trip she had been truly attracted to him and had even seriously considered marrying him after a few weeks, if he had asked her. Now his increasing possessiveness and taking her for granted had turned her off. True, without a man the future looked bleak, but his easily aroused anger gave her no choice.

As she realized she would need a man to help her manage her lands, she also knew she should not turn to the Picos or others for aid. Perhaps she could be of use at the mission for the time being. At least the return would not be in the dead of winter. Depressed and lonely as she had been when her husband died, long-held-back tears fell silently.

Some fell on Tomasa's hands around her mother's waist. "Don't cry, *Mamá*. Are you sick? We need you." Tomasa nestled closer. "I'll help you."

Feliciana shook her head. It was no time to cry. "Thank you, *querida mía*. I guess I'm just tired. I haven't anything to cry about when I have you and Eustaquía."

So, silently and depressed, Feliciana and Gallardo followed Anza down the *cañon* side. Gradually the high walls gave way to small hills and then opened onto a great meadow that overlooked a valley below.

As the caravan stopped, Tomasa threw back the blanket. "Look *Mamá*, look," she cried. "No snow!"

One thousand feet below them stretched the valley. Instead of the seemingly endless snow, there was now a lake sparkling in the sun. They could see excellent pasturage and plenty of firewood from the surrounding live oaks. Feliciana could only stare, sure it must be a mirage. Even up here the sun gave off a warmth that dispelled their depression. Quickly they made camp.

Tomasa and Eustaquía soon brought Feliciana hands full of sweet aromatic rosemary and even a few sunflowers. Other children were busy gathering the pungent herb with its blue flowers.

After supper *Padre* Font walked among them and, wonder of wonders, Feliciana noted he had no limp. He had been out on the meadow and was full of enthusiasm.

"This place should be named for Anza," he said, showing them other small flowers he had found. "We must stay here at least for another night. I will speak to *el Capitán* about it."

With an important air he stepped up to the leader. Together the two walked outside the campfire area. Feliciana and Jacinta looked at each other in surprise. Rarely had the two men gone off for a walk before on such apparently friendly terms.

Font returned with good humor spilling over. He smiled and said Anza was going to follow his suggestion, and then went on to his tent.

"What miracle is this?" asked *Señor* Pico of all who were nearby. "It must be a miracle—the miracle of California!" Could California have a miracle for her, Feliciana wondered. Not likely, she decided.

Even though they did push on the next day, Font retained his good humor. The descent to the valley still held treacherous boulders and slippery paths, but no one minded. They were in California—the California that Anza had spoken of. They had seen the worst and survived.

Had the turquoise stone really helped? Feliciana doubted it.

106

CHAPTER 22

They camped that night near the lake seen from above. The boys came back quite excited from their nightly task of gathering firewood. These great oaks held their leaves all winter and the vines looked like they might bear grapes. With the vast number of wildflowers already seen, it was truly a land of bounty. At last Anza's promise seemed real, Feliciana thought.

"This would be a wonderful place to stay," said Jacinta Pico as they sat by the campfire that night. "Sheep could live here, the kind that come from Spain. So much water— I think it should be called Paradise Valley."

Feliciana agreed with the name, but knew in her mind it was not the place for a lone woman who knew nothing about growing crops or cattle or sheep.

It was hard to leave the next morning, but San Gabriel lay not far ahead, Anza reminded them. They were still tired, but the depression was gone. True, many walked because their horses were either dead or too exhausted, and what few cattle were left were walking skeletons. But there was a halting place not far ahead.

As in a dream, Feliciana moved across the flower-covered land toward the Santa Ana River, which Anza had said would be the last one. Everyone seemed relaxed— complacent even—because they had seen and crossed many other rivers. So they were totally unprepared for the rushing torrent that met their eyes and ears.

When Feliciana saw the river she almost turned Gallardo around in the other direction. It wasn't fair, she wanted to cry; so near the end of the journey and then this raging river. She remembered the crossing of the Colorado. It was a quiet one compared to this, but even so she had almost lost Tomasa.

She heard Anza's call to halt here for the night—so she could have nightmares about this last crossing? Just hearing Anza's voice, though, reminded her that he had never disappointed them. Perhaps she wouldn't have to make Gallardo carry them through this torrent; perhaps there was another way, a miracle way.

Feliciana sighed. This was no time to give up. She prided herself that she had never given up, once she had given a promise. Her head ached, unusual for her. Perhaps this made her less able to cope with one more problem.

When she had heard Anza call a halt for the night, they had traveled seven hours that day. It was New Years Eve and Anza ordered out the brandy keg to celebrate. Feliciana noticed Font gave no sign he had heard.

"It's hard to think this is the end of the year," *Señor* Pico said as the group gathered at supper. "I wonder where we will be next year at this time."

Feliciana declared, "It certainly must be under better conditions. The good *Capitán* assures us all will be well. But I'm not sure I would have come if I had known there would be so many hardships."

There was silence. All thought of the forced marches, the days with little water, and the terrible cold. Now the year was past and they could celebrate.

The small *fiesta* almost wiped out their food supplies, but who cared? They would soon be in San Gabriel, and they had survived!

The singing and dancing were more constrained that night. Feliciana sang, but danced little. This might be her last *fiesta* with these friends, and she felt depressed both physically and mentally.

Don Muños finally snatched her from her partner in the middle of the last dance and took her to one side.

"Why have you been avoiding me?" he demanded. "I still want to marry you. How can you make a living here without a husband? Your children need a father. Tomasa especially, since she was chosen Mary in the *Posada*, has ignored me when I have corrected her. Both children are getting out of hand. Be reasonable, *Doña* Feliciana; think of your family, if you won't think of yourself."

Feliciana stepped back. "I have been thinking of them. I've decided to return to Horcasitas and my family. I don't want to marry you, and the children definitely don't want you for a father. I thought I had made myself clear about this before."

"No. I know you are a very beautiful woman, very desirable and in need of a man to tame your wild streak. With a firm hand you would make a wonderful wife. We both have land coming at the end, and we could have a large spread. We would be rich and have many people working for us. Think about this."

She backed farther away. "My answer is still NO! At this time there is no one I wish to marry—no one who would be a good father to my girls. It must be their choice as well as mine. I do thank you for the help you have given me on the journey, but I do not wish to marry you. Good night." She stepped quickly away and went to her tent. His face told her how angry he was, and she knew how he acted at such times.

Feliciana slept little that night. She had finally made up her mind to return. Was it only to be free of *Señor* Muños? But he would be impossible as a husband. These months on her own had been wonderful. That reminded her that if she went home she would be under her father's will again. If he should die, then her brother would take his place.

Perhaps if she spoke to *Padre* Font he could help her, but immediately she rejected the idea. He would tell her to marry *Señor* Muños, she was sure. Perhaps *el capitán* could help. These thoughts churned over and over in her mind. At last she decided to tell no one yet. They would stay at San Gabriel for a few days and perhaps she could decide by then.

After a restless sleep, Feliciana awoke feeling ill both in body and mind. She had kept well through all the time that others had been sick. Why now, she wondered, when San Gabriel was so near?

109

CHAPTER 23

New Years Day Feliciana sat through the mass feeling dizzy and hearing little of *Padre* Font's sermon. If she had been listening she would have heard no mention of the *fiesta*. There were no scoldings for the brandy and dancing—nor for a young widow.

Instead he reminded them of the day and what the future could hold for them. *Padre* Font was in a relaxed, happy state. Definitely the California miracle had affected him.

While the people were at mass, apparently Anza had surveyed the river. His bridge of the year before needed repairs, and a road would be needed also to get the cattle down and into the water for crossing.

As the colonists came from the service, Anza called to them, "I need some men to help. This is the bridge we built last year. We can repair it in a little while if you all help."

Feliciana watched, dizzy and definitely ill, as strong heavy green vines were gathered. These were used to tie the bridge sections together. Although it had never been more than a makeshift crossing, Anza now rode across the weaving structure to show it was safe enough for the people to use. They could walk or ride on their horses, but the rest of the animals would have to swim. Though turbulent, the river wasn't deep.

Once on the other side the women gathered together and the men went for firewood. Feliciana herself had barely made it across the bridge. Gallardo at first was reluctant and tested each step as the bridge swayed. The girls held on tightly, but all Feliciana could do was stare down at the water rushing so close underneath.

"Look up, look up," someone cried. "Trust your horse." Feliciana tried and found the going easier, but was relieved when Gallardo walked on solid ground again.

Feliciana joined the women. The unsteadiness had upset many of them, and they were crying and wondering what was next. She sympathized with them and then moved on near to Jacinta. As soon as the tent was up she told Jacinta she would rest and hope the dizziness would go away.

"How much more must we take?" Feliciana murmured to Jacinta. "I hope this is the last of our troubles."

"I'll take the girls with me. You rest," Jacinta told her. "We'll stay outside."

Feliciana had just dozed off when she became aware of a commotion by the river. The girls called her to come and watch. A bull was floundering in the rough water. Feliciana saw it was too weak and exhausted to help itself, and the men were trying to get a rope around its neck. Just as the rope settled over his head the bull gave a convulsive shudder and sank. Horse and rider were pulled under with him as the onlookers screamed. The man surfaced almost immediately and, to Feliciana's relief, several ropes were thrown to him. Many hands helped pull him ashore, but the bull and horse, tangled in the *lasso*, were swept rapidly downstream.

A stunned silence fell over the whole group. Feliciana could take no more, and fled back into the tent. The drama had happened so suddenly, just as they had supposed all obstacles were past.

Fires were made silently and the smell of damp clothes drying hung over the camp as the meal simmered. There was little talk that afternoon.

Feliciana was still dozing when Tomasa flew into the tent to say a lot of horses and men had just ridden into the camp. Feliciana was too curious to stay inside, and as she emerged, a strange soldier came by. She stared at him, amazed, for he was the first person she had seen lately who had not looked haggard and half-ill, or who was not dressed in stained travel-worn clothes.

Hastily she apologized. "Forgive me for staring. It is so long since I have seen anyone who looks so well." Tomasa stood beside her. She too seemed fascinated with the stranger.

The soldier's round face with deep brown eyes wavered and faded—and Feliciana suddenly slid to the ground in a faint.

"*Mamá!*" cried Tomasa, dropping down beside Feliciana.

The stranger looked around helplessly until *Señora* Pico rushed from the tent. More women came, and soon Feliciana was sitting up, perplexed at the confusion.

"Are you all right, Feliciana?" asked Jacinta. "Shall I call *Capitán* Anza?"

Before Feliciana could answer there was a bump and a cry behind the soldier. Eustaquía, seeing the people in front of her tent, had come rushing towards them and had tripped. When the newcomer reached down to help her up, Eustaquía saw the strange face and screamed again. Feliciana reached out her arms for the little girl.

Anza arrived just then, about to reprimand the soldier for disturbing the women. But Feliciana stopped him.

"I'm sorry, *Capitán* Anza, it is all my fault. I must have fainted and that has upset my girls. This poor soldier has done nothing but help Eustaquía up from a fall."

The soldier saluted Anza. "I am Juan Francisco López, *Capitán*, one of the group that brought the horses from San Gabriel. I'm sorry I startled the young *señora.*" He turned to Feliciana. "I apologize if *I* stared. It has been so long since I've seen a young woman from my country."

"I well understand you staring at our lovely young *Señora* Feliciana Arballo," said Anza. "This is her Tomasa, and the little one you picked up is Eustaquía, a young favorite of mine. Be careful, young man; she is very particular about whom she likes, eh *mi niñita!*" and he ruffled Eustaquía's curly hair.

"As for you, young lady, I didn't know you were ill. It's good we are staying overnight. San Gabriel has sent us seventeen fresh horses, and we'll decide who is to use them."

Feliciana was quite chagrined at her weakness. She had never fainted before in her life.

Crossing the California Desert

"We are all stretched too tight," commented *Doña* Jacinta. "It will be good to reach the mission, where I hope we can stay for a bit. Even here, with plenty of food and water, it is good for the animals. Go back inside and rest, Feliciana."

Feliciana lay thinking of the courteous stranger. Not like *Don* Muños; but all the men were by now too tired for even polite conversation. His smooth-shaven face contrasted with Anza's bearded one, but both had those warm friendly brown eyes. Anza too was showing deep lines of fatigue and strain. Surely the stranger would see them as wretched prospective colonists. Again she dozed as the camp went about its business.

Later Anza came to speak with her. "How are you? Would you like another day of rest?"

"I'm fine now, thank you," Feliciana assured him. "Gallardo and I can hold out now. Don't worry any more about me."

"Well, I'm suggesting that López ride near you tomorrow anyway. I don't want you falling and scaring us again." Anza patted her shoulder and went on.

The next morning Juan López rode up as the Picos finished packing.

"*Buenos días, señora*. Are you better today? Is your husband ready to leave?" He dismounted as he spoke.

Feliciana was startled. She realized no one had told him she was a widow, but *Señor* Pico had overheard.

"*Señora* Arballo travels alone with her children, young man. Her husband died fighting the Apaches. She has been a brave young woman who asks for little help."

"Again I apologize," and the young soldier blushed a deep red. "I seem to do or say the wrong things. I'm so sorry."

Feliciana smiled. "There's nothing to be sorry for. I appreciate you riding with us, but don't feel I will be a burden on you. I'm much better today." She motioned to her two girls. "This is Tomasa and this is Eustaquía. Don't mind if Eustaquía stays away from you—she seems to have a fear of men. She only goes to *Capitán* Anza and *Señor* Pico. Do you have a family?" It was Feliciana's turn to be embarrassed as she remembered him saying he had

114

not seen a white woman for a long time.

The soldier laughed pleasantly. "Oh no. I am not married, and I hope I don't scare you, Eustaquía," he added, turning to the four-year-old.

She looked him over soberly. "You picked me up," she stated, and then turned her slow sweet smile on him. "You nice man, like Anza. I Anza's girl."

Feliciana chuckled, surprised again at this child of hers. Already Tomasa was in her place, accepting help from the stranger with no qualms.

"Will you let *Señor* López hand you up to me?" she asked Eustaquía.

"*Sí Mamá.* He nice man."

Feliciana, aided by the soldier, for she was still a little weak, stepped up to her saddle. Gravely, López lifted Eustaquía up to her mother and said, "Thank you, young lady."

As they rode along after the singing of the *Alabado*, Feliciana glanced furtively at her companion. His manners were unusual for a soldier. Though not overly tall, he appeared so in the saddle. His friendly smile suggested a peaceful nature. She guessed he was about Anza's age.

How was it that a four-year-old would accept him with just one meeting and refuse another? Anyhow, it was pleasant to have a friendly relaxed person riding beside her and not the turbulent Muños.

The sky darkened as they rode, and soon heavy rain began falling. They were climbing through low hills and the ground was slippery and muddy.

Señor López came close and swung his long heavy cape around the three on Gallardo. He took the reins from Feliciana and led them through a bad stretch of road.

The thoughtful gestures brought tears to Feliciana's eyes. "What is the matter with me," she thought. "I must be weak, but never has anyone shown me such kindnesses as on this trip."

Feliciana called to the soldier. "But you will get wet," she said.

He turned and smiled. "You have been ill, *Señora,* and the little ones need cover. Besides, I have my leather jacket on. *Es nada,*" and he rode on.

She looked at the straight back in front of her. It was such a strong broad back, as though it could carry many burdens. Eustaquía had said he was like Anza, who certainly had been kind to all who needed help. She thought of the many times he had delayed a departure so that those who were ill might recover. He had carried small children to relieve tired mothers. When he aided at a birth the woman adored him.

Mostly the men in Feliciana's life hadn't been like that. Her father loved them, but he made the laws of the house, and everyone must obey him. José too had been a loving father and husband, but meals were to be on time and his clothes always ready when he needed them. *Doña* Jacinta had said it was a man's world, and Feliciana realized all of the women accepted that without protest.

This was no day for reasoning, Feliciana decided. The rain was letting up. Eustaquía must be asleep, she leaned so heavily against her. Tomasa pressed against her back. Feliciana relaxed and slept a little too, glad that Gallardo was being led by someone who seemed to care about others.

SAN GABRIEL

CHAPTER 24

Señor Pico asked Juan López to have supper with them. The rain had finally stopped and Anza had chosen to camp under the trees.

After supper Feliciana sat quietly near the fire, trying to dry the soldier's cape as the others talked.

"I understand we will be staying at the mission for a little while. Is that right?" Pico asked *Señor* López. "Something about trouble at San Diego, isn't it?"

"*Sí Señor* Pico. The Indians in that area have seized the mission. They killed the *padre* and two servants."

Horrified, Feliciana looked at Jacinta. She knew her friend was frightened of Indians, no matter where they were. She turned back to hear the rest of the story.

"We were told to tell *Capitán* Anza that *Comandante* Rivera is afraid the uprising will spread to San Gabriel. He wishes the *capitán* to put down this rebellion at San Diego."

"And what do you think, *Señor* López?" asked Pico. "What are the Indians like at San Gabriel? Will we be in any danger staying there?"

Feliciana and Jacinta listened anxiously.

The soldier smiled. "*Señor*, one never knows for sure what the Indians will do. I have been at both missions, first at San Diego and then coming here when San Gabriel was started in 1771. The Indians are quite different types. Also, our *padre* has a different way of working with the natives."

This interested Feliciana. Sometimes the *padre* sets the standard for his workers.

"What is it like at your mission?" asked one. "Is it in a barren area?" questioned another. "Are there good fields for crops and cattle?"

Everyone around the fire listened eagerly for the answers. Anza had told them it was good, but they were hungry for news from one who lived there.

"It is the best in California," Juan López said simply. His tone spoke eloquently of his love of the area. "We have wonderful weather, good crops, much land for cattle, sheep and horses. There is fishing in the river and hunting in the hills that are not too far away.

"*Padre* Paterna is a very understanding person, but also strict about rules. He does not punish unless it is necessary, and then it fits the misdeed."

There was a big sigh around the fire. After the last weeks it seemed impossible to think they were almost to this paradise. Feliciana looked forward to meeting this *padre*. Was he like *Padre* Garcés? Evidently López approved of him.

"But how many Indians are there around there?" asked *Señora* Pico.

"About 500 live around the mission compound in small huts. They are the ones who have been converted. *Padre* Paterno finds it better for them. They are not allowed to leave except for special reasons.

"If they do leave without permission, we must go and bring them back. Then they are punished; extra work, perhaps, but never whipped."

Feliciana relaxed, remembering the cries of the whipped muleteers. She realized the crimes really were not comparable. She looked up and saw Juan's eyes on her. Impulsively she smiled at him, glad that the soldier seemed to approve of gentle ways. Quickly she lowered her eyes and shifted the drying cape while someone else spoke up.

"Who does the work at the mission?"

"The *padres* train the natives to cook, clean and do all the work that needs doing. These are gentle Indians and happy to please. You will see," and the soldier smiled confidently. "It's a really pleasant place to work and live." Feliciana felt he was again looking her way. A quick glance confirmed her thought and she blushed unexpectedly. No one had looked at her so warmly and personally in a long, long time.

He was plied with many questions for a time. Then he excused himself to return to where the soldiers were camped for the night.

Shyly Feliciana handed him the cape that was now nearly dry. "Thank you again, *Señor* López. I am much better now, especially when I hear what a lovely place your mission must be. Tomorrow the girls and I will manage all right."

"Are you sure, *Señora*? If in the morning you are not well, *Capitán* Anza can arrange for me to stay with you." He paused as though he would add some other thought, but went on, "The mission soldiers are riding straight through with messages. The way to the mission is easy from here. I will see you in San Gabriel, I'm sure. Thank you for caring for my cape." As he took it from her, his hands closed over hers for a moment. Feliciana felt a tingle of communication. Did he affect all women this way, she wondered?

She rejoined the Picos, sure the blush was still on her face. But Jacinta was speaking and paying no attention.

"I feel much better now. I was so afraid we were going to have to stay here through an Indian uprising. But I do want to stay long enough to rest and wash clothes. And I hope the sun shines a lot."

"I know I will feel better, too," Feliciana said, "when it's sunny and I'm warm again."

The ride the next day was uneventful and Feliciana felt more like her usual self. Though it rained lightly off and on, they rode through pleasant meadows among the low rolling hills. New grass was springing up among the rosemary shrubs and in every crevice that had been brown. As the animals' hooves brushed the grey-green plants, the sharp sweet fragrance mingled with the fresh rain-washed air. She thought of *Señor* López and what he had said last night about this being a wonderful place. Was it because the air was freshening her body as well as the plants, or because waiting at the mission was a warm friendly person?

All dizziness was gone and she breathed deeply, glad to

be alive. Seldom had they had such rain in Sonora and never enough to make the grass so green nor the flowers so vibrant in color.

When doubts about her future arose, she quickly pushed them aside. Then came a sudden somber thought: did Juan López have a girl waiting for him somewhere? Then the girls were tugging at her.

"*Mamá*," said Tomasa, patting her on the shoulder. "Were you asleep? Everyone is stopping."

"Tell Gallardo 'stop,' *Mamá*," said Eustaquía. "I want down."

Feliciana came out of her reverie. It was true, the others had stopped, and obedient Gallardo was just walking around them until he had orders to stop.

"Are you all right, *Mamá*?" asked Tomasa. "Were you asleep?" They had never seen Feliciana ill before.

She laughed. "I'm fine now. I was just thinking about so many other things, I didn't notice. Did you girls see the lovely green grass and all the flowers? It's so clean, and not dusty."

They stopped early that day by the San Gabriel Wash. Feliciana was glad for the extra time before they would arrive at the mission tomorrow about noon. She needed time to wash some clothes and her hair. It looked so limp since she was ill. They would be greeting *Padre* Paterna and the *comandante* of Monterey, *Don* Fernando Rivera y Moncada, who was there because of the trouble at San Diego.

Gallardo looked better, not so many ribs showing, she thought as she brushed him. She brought out fresh yellow ribbons for the girls and the horse and noticed others were doing the same. She was sure they all wanted to do Anza proud when they rode into San Gabriel. But after looking over most of the colonists with their still wan and strained faces, she knew it would take more time.

Their spirits were good, though. They all laughed and sang with Feliciana after supper. They had survived and nothing could stop them now—especially with friends already waiting for them at the mission. "At least one is, I hope," she thought to herself.

As they settled for this last night, Tomasa asked her mother, "How long will we stay here? This isn't San Francisco Bay, is it?"

"No, *niñita*, there's a long way to go yet. We will stay at different missions—all in California. *Capitán* Anza says he has sent them word that we are coming and have little food left."

Feliciana had decided not to tell the children about her thoughts of going back to Sonora. She was sure it would make them unhappy after the long hard trip to get here. There might be a better time later, and who knows what could happen in the meantime. Maybe a California miracle, she thought wryly.

Sleeping was difficult that night. Tomorrow I'll see my first California mission, Feliciana thought. Would there be Indians all around, as by the Colorado? Would there be plenty of water? Would there be plenty of food—ours is almost gone. The soldier assured us, though, that we would have plenty to eat. She was sure others were also worrying on this last night before San Gabriel.

Though sleep was slow coming, she waked early. So did most of the others, and *Padre* Font took advantage of that and held an extra long mass. Feliciana wished he would hurry, but he reminded them of all they had to be grateful for—they had survived rivers, Indians, the deserts and the freezing mountains.

Strong voices joined Feliciana as they sang the *Alabado*. They were on the last lap of their journey into California.

Just as the sun was overhead, Feliciana heard the mission bell. This was a real one, and not like the ones in her dream at Tubac.

When she saw *Padre* Paterna and the *comandante* riding towards them, Feliciana's heart gave a great leap. Surely something good was coming in the days ahead. Gallardo gave a jump when the guns boomed out a salute—what a welcome, Feliciana thought. After 74 days it was like being welcomed home. The rest of the trip north now seemed like an anti-climax.

She and the girls slid from Gallardo as the mission bells rang and rang, calling the soldiers and workers in to meet them.

Feliciana felt sure they must be presenting a sorry sight in spite of all the brushings and ribbons. Everyone greeted them with smiles though, as if they had never seen a finer group. Feliciana looked around as best she could, but saw no sight of a special soldier, so she guessed he was busy elsewhere.

Then the kitchen workers led the colonists to long tables loaded with food. As they ate, Feliciana was sure she had never had such delicious lamb stew as this, with its fresh tasting vegetables. She thought of the tough stringy beef they had endured so long.

"Can't eat any more, *Mamá*," said Eustaquía, leaning against her, ready for a nap. She had had her first custard and fresh bread in months. Even Tomasa admitted she had enjoyed the vegetables.

"Let's stay here, *Mamá*," said Tomasa, gazing at the still loaded tables.

Feliciana heard similar remarks from others as they lingered over cups of wine from the small vineyard.

When Anza called for attention, Feliciana eased Eustaquía's head down into her lap for a nap.

"I'm leaving in a couple of days for the San Diego mission with *Comandante* Rivera. I'll take seventeen of our soldiers to give what assistance they may need there. Lieutenant Moraga will be in charge while I'm gone."

"So choose your places for your tents, near the small creek if you wish. *Padre* Paterna says he has some supplies, though not ample, and you may ask him for what you need. I'll see you in the morning and answer any questions you may have. *Buenas noches!*"

Feliciana was pleased when *Señor* Pico chose a spot quite distant from the compound set aside for the Indians. *Señora* Pico still had a fear of a sudden uprising and wanted plenty of space around her.

There were many live oaks in the valley. Feliciana was thankful they were to be here for awhile. It was a lovely place with trees and a small stream and a chance to really rest after the weeks just past.

"Are there other Indians near here?" Tomasa asked her mother that night. Some of the children had rather warily scouted around the mission area later in the afternoon.

"Oh yes. The ones you see live here, but there are many others among the hills, I'm sure."

"I saw all the older girls were dressed like we are—with blouses and skirts. They weren't afraid of us either. They smiled and said hello in Spanish."

"The *padres* have taught them to speak Spanish," Feliciana explained. "They must understand when he gives them orders and teaches them their catechism. Of course there are some who can translate when new Indians arrive."

"They came up and touched our faces. 'So white,' they said." Tomasa giggled. "The little girls wanted to look at our legs too. I guess they wondered if we were white all over. But they tickled us, and when we laughed they laughed too."

Solemnly Eustaquía stretched out a curl and let it snap back. Feliciana joined in their laughter.

"They touched our hair," explained Tomasa. "They pulled out our curls and watched them snap back. I guess they've never seen curly hair before. Their hair is straight, but I don't want to touch it. It looks greasy and dirty."

Feliciana thought it likely they had lice and mites in it too. The three looked inside the now familiar tent. It was bedtime, but it was so pleasant outside, no one wanted to go in. They watched the soldiers from the mission rounding up the Indian workers from the far fields. Hard as she tried, Feliciana could see no soldier who resembled the one who had cared for them during the rain.

"To bed, girls," she finally said. "There is so much to see, I know, but there will be many more days to explore."

To herself she thought how happily she could stay here. Would she really see Juan López again? Perhaps he would go south with Anza. The thought depressed her as though she was being deserted. Mentally she shook herself. How silly could she get? If he did go south, then he would return.

Anyhow, she didn't have to go on with the others. Tomorrow was another day—new things to see and do. As she drifted off to sleep she thought again of the concern in a pair of brown eyes and the touch of a hand.

CHAPTER 25

The pleasant weather held for another day. Feliciana and the girls walked over towards the mission. Anza had told them it had been moved since he was here last. Then it had been nearer to San Gabriel Wash, but heavy rains had forced the *padres* to choose a place that, while near water, would not be flooded.

This new site had many possibilities, Feliciana thought. The present buildings looked hastily built, yet space had been left for more Indian huts. There were several small structures in a row. Some of these must be for food supplies. A corral for the horses was nearby, and then another long low building near the mission. She wondered what it was for, especially when she saw the now open door could be bolted from the inside.

The girls wanted to walk through the Indian section, although there were only mothers and small children in sight. They stopped beside a mother with a tiny baby.

"Isn't the baby darling, girls?"

"How old?" she asked the mother.

Shyly she answered, "*Uno mes, Señora.*"

Small children crowded around them, gazing in awe. Feliciana held out her arms to the baby of another mother who had come close. Feliciana asked if she might hold the child, perhaps six months old.

After only a moment's hesitation the mother handed her the baby, wrapped in a piece of rough blanket. The *padres* had insisted on clothing even for the babies, Feliciana chuckled to herself. She cradled it lovingly—so long since Eustaquía had been this small. Feliciana wondered if she would ever have another little one.

"Let me hold the baby too, *Mamá*," asked Tomasa, softly touching a little brown hand.

"Not this time, *niñita*. We mustn't scare the baby's *mamá*." She handed the little one back to the smiling mother, while the baby only regarded them with a blank impassive stare.

A glance around the huts showed these were only for sleeping. No fires for cooking showed, because the mission fed all the converts. The dresses of the little girls, perhaps long blouses of older sisters, were dirty and torn. Apparently no one was concerned about cleanliness or health for these poor people. Feliciana was glad to head back to the fresh-smelling campsite of the Picos.

They continued their walk along the small stream. Many plants grew here and Feliciana recognized celery, parsnips and turnips. In the quiet edges were bright green watercress. These plants had been pointed out to her along one of the other rivers on the trip, but here they were abundant and promised that many other plants would thrive here too. The great oaks on the hillsides gave a look of lush growth such as Feliciana had never seen before. It was obvious that the mission could grow much of what it needed.

As they sat at the noon meal, *Señor* Pico told of going to the mission storehouse where the *padre* and his helpers had distributed some grain and corn to the newcomers. Thinking of the fine land, Feliciana realized it took several years to get fields into full production and so become independent of the homeland.

Pico verified this when he said the storerooms were not full. "They have been waiting for supplies from San Diego for a long time. Now the uprising has probably destroyed much of what they had. *Padre* Paterna was generous, but he reminded us that he had 500 Indians and soldiers to feed. Maybe Anza will bring back some food."

"It's too bad the *capitán* has to go so soon," said Feliciana. "He looks so exhausted, and *Padre* Font is ill again too."

Privately she agreed when Jacinta said, "I don't like that *Comandante* Rivera. He walks about as though he owned the place and was being kind to let us stay here. I'll be glad to see him go."

One of the Pico boys spoke up: "*Padre* Font is angry too. He says Anza had told him to stay here and get well."

During the laughter that followed a soldier from the mission rode up. Feliciana recognized him immediately as the one who had cared for her and the girls in the rain. She saw he had business with Santiago Pico, so sat quietly. Would he remember her?

"I'm just checking to see if you got your supplies from the mission storehouse," Juan López said. "Is everything all right?"

"We are more than happy here. Your *padre* has certainly made us feel at home."

Feliciana knew he spoke for her as well as the others.

"This is my assignment, to look after you." Then he saw Feliciana and his face lit up. "And how are you, *Señora?*"

"Oh I'm fine now, *Señor* López. It is certainly a beautiful place, just as you said."

"I'm sorry I didn't see you last night, but we were busy getting *Capitán* Anza's trip arranged. We are worried about *Padre* Font, who insists he must go."

Pico laughed. "Just try and keep *Padre* Font here, even though Anza told him to stay. Thank you for stopping by."

"My pleasure," the soldier said. Feliciana met his eyes and he seemed to be saying he would see her again—and soon. Is it the contrast with Muños that makes this mission soldier seem so special, she wondered?

When the soldier had gone on, Pico remarked, "I'm impressed with the soldiers at this post. *Padre* Paterna is apparently a most unusual man. I hear he has a special building where the girls and older single women live— it's called the nunnery. Few missions have thought to protect and care for the girls and young women as he does."

Feliciana felt a renewing of her decision to stay here until Anza returned from San Francisco Bay. With a kind *padre* and such a thoughtful soldier as Juan López around, she would have no harrassment from any such as Muños.

Even as she was thinking that, *Señor* Peralta spoke up. "I heard that Anza is taking *Don* Muños with him to San Diego. I hope he doesn't stir up any trouble there. Few of Anza's men like him. He certainly is not of the caliber of men stationed here. He's always picking quarrels lately, I understand."

Feliciana tried to appear disinterested, but secretly it was most welcome news. Now she could really relax and enjoy this peaceful place.

She was out early the next morning to watch Anza, Rivera and the chosen soldiers ride out of camp. When she saw Muños wave, she turned her head away.

"And there is *Padre* Font," pointed Dolores Pico with a grin. "I heard that Rivera told Font he was sending Anza back to Mexico and he, Rivera, would take us to San Francisco Bay. Font told Anza, and immediately Anza said he would be happy to have Font with him. Nobody would separate them."

"Wherever do you hear all these things, Dolores?" asked his mother. But Dolores just grinned.

It was quiet after the men left. Feliciana happily took the time to sort and mend clothes. She watched the children enjoying real freedom. Her girls and Gertrudis played with the half-grown kittens, laughing and tumbling them about. Somehow they and their mother had survived the rough winter and their coats had grown thick and warm.

Heavy clouds had begun forming one morning when Juan López stopped and asked for the young *señora*. Feliciana stepped out of the tent, surprised and pleased to see him.

"*Señora, Padre* Paterna and I have been speaking of you. The *padre* would say this himself, but you must understand he is quite shy around beautiful young women. So he asked me to do the talking.

"We have a proposition to make. You are here alone— no," he put his hand up as she made a move to interrupt, "I understand you have shared the tent with these people from the beginning. Please think about this. Our Indian girls and young women sleep in the nunnery. There they are protected from the rain and the soldiers. There will be more rain—and very soon," he added with a glance at the sky. "Would you and your girls like to move into the nunnery while you wait for *el Capitán* to return? Don't answer now. I'll stop by and see you later."

He was gone before she could thank him for thinking

about her. It was getting crowded in the tent, now that they were not on the road all day.

Seeing that *Doña* Jacinta had overheard the offer, Feliciana turned to her. "It sounds enticing," she confessed. "It would be nice to be out of the rain, but do you think the Indian girls would like an intruder?"

"Feliciana, we have enjoyed having you with us and I'm sure these young girls will too, especially if you sing to them. Maybe you could show them how to wash and keep clean. They look as though no one had ever taken much care of them." *Doña* Jacinta shook her head. "I must confess they smell as though a bath now and then wouldn't hurt. Maybe you could have some good influence over them."

All day Feliciana went over the offer in her mind. She took Eustaquía and Tomasa with her and walked over to what she now knew was the nunnery. The door was open, and they stepped inside. The room had some roughly made cots along one wall. Many heavy-woven blankets were piled against the other. All was neat, but the hard-packed dirt floor needed a good sweeping.

"Would you like to sleep here at night with me and the Indian girls?" she asked them.

"If we stayed in here our blankets would be dry," Tomasa shrewdly noted. "But would these girls like us here?"

"That's what we would have to find out," answered her mother. "Perhaps if they saw me brush your hair they might brush theirs. They wouldn't like us to make fun of them, I'm sure, but then I don't think you would anyway. Shall we try it for a few nights? We can always go back to the Picos if we wish."

"I'd like to try it," said Tomasa.

"Me too," said Eustaquía.

"Me too," echoed their mother, and they laughed together. She explained that the nice soldier who had helped her when she was ill had suggested this idea.

Later that afternoon Juan López came back. Feliciana was startled to see Eustaquía rush up and seize his hand.

"We're going to sleep with Indians," she announced.

He glanced at Feliciana, who nodded her head and said, "I had planned to say 'thank you very much, we would be happy to accept your offer,' but Eustaquía has done it quite simply." She shook her head. "Eustaquía is most surprising. Only with men she knows well does she respond like this. What shall we bring? The boys here say they will carry our things for us."

López summoned some Indian boys, and together with the Picos they moved Feliciana's blankets and bags to the new building. There were only a few high windows and the open door to let in light, so they hurried to finish before dark.

As they entered the nunnery shortly before dusk, the Indian girls stared in surprise. To Feliciana's amusement, a somewhat flustered *Señor* López explained that the *señora* and her daughters would be sleeping in the nunnery for awhile.

After his few words and *buenas noches* to all, he hastily left. Apparently he wasn't used to being alone with these young women either.

They all stared at each other. Then one girl came over and fingered Eustaquía's curls, pulling them down and then releasing them. That broke the ice and everyone laughed. The Indians stared as Tomasa and her sister took off their blouses and skirts and put on night shifts. They watched, puzzled, as Feliciana brushed her girls' hair and then her own.

She motioned to a girl about ten to come to her. As she started to lift the child's hair to brush it, she was pushed aside with a "No, no!" Feliciana sighed.

"All right for tonight. Tomorrow we will talk about such things."

She saw each girl knew where she slept. The older Indians spread their blankets on the cots and the younger ones put theirs on the floor. Then they lay watching the newcomers. Feliciana knew none had ever seen a white woman before.

She had been given one of the cots and she spread her sheepskin over the rope springs, followed by her blankets. She put her girls' blankets on each side of her on the floor.

The three knelt to say their prayers. Part way through, a murmur came from the room as all joined in. Feliciana felt a thrill at the first real communication.

As darkness filled the building—whose door Feliciana had barred as instructed—she started singing softly. The buzzing of the natives grew quieter and quieter. When Felician stopped, a small contented sigh floated through the room. They were accepted!

Tomasa and Eustaquía reached hands up to her. Tomasa whispered, "They liked it! Just like when you first sang in the Picos' tent."

Waiting for sleep, Feliciana thought there was something strange about all this. Why had she been asked to sleep here? Was the soldier really the one who had planned this? Surely there were others, like *Señora* Linares and her new baby, who needed protection from the rain.

Feliciana thought again of the day Juan López had put his cape around them to protect them from the rain. She remembered the warm caring look in his eyes and his smile when he said, "You have been ill, *Señora*, and the little ones need cover."

Muños might throw a cape around her—and himself, no doubt—but never for the children's sake, she was sure.

Rain pattered softly on the roof and lulled Feliciana to sleep, happy to know someone cared. *Padre* Paterna? Juan López?

CHAPTER 26

The pealing of the bells announced a new day. It took Feliciana a few moments to remember where she was. Her two girls tugged at her.

"Time to get up, *Mamá*," Tomasa said. "The others are folding their blankets."

Already many of the girls had left for the kitchen work. Quickly Feliciana joined the rest as they gathered outside where *Padre* Paterna stood waiting to say the morning prayers.

Ya viene el alba rompienda el dia
Dígamos, "Ave María."
(Here comes the dawn tearing into the sky,
Let us all sing "Ave Maria."

After the chant each one took her bowl and cup to be served *atole* and hot chocolate.

"How did you like starting the day with these girls?" asked Feliciana of Tomasa and Eustaquía later on.

"It's nice, *Mamá*," said Tomasa. "We don't have to get wood for the fire and you don't have to cook breakfast."

"It's nice," agreed her mother, "but I must find some way to earn this. Also, tomorrow we must get up promptly so you can wash your hands and face and get your hair brushed. It looks like we shall have to get organized ourselves, or we will be just like these Indian girls."

Eustaquía made a face. "I like this way. I like to be Indian girl."

Her mother laughed. "Not with those curls. In a few days I would have to cut off all your hair, it would be so tangled. Come on, let's get cleaned up now for the day."

After she and the girls had folded their blankets and put them on Feliciana's bed, they walked over to see the Picos.

"How did it go?" asked *Doña* Jacinta. "Do you wish some breakfast?"

"No, thank you. We ate with the girls from the nunnery. *Padre* Paterna said we might join them if we wished. I thought it was a good time to show that we were all the same."

"How was your bed? Did they resent you sleeping with them?"

"No. They were puzzled at first. They watched me brush Eustaquía's hair but didn't want me to brush theirs. You were right, Jacinta, there is much I can do if they will let me." Feliciana laughed. "I overslept this morning, and we didn't wash before prayers or breakfast. Eustaquía thought that was just fine. She says she would like to be an Indian."

"Well, don't hurry it. If you keep yourselves clean, they will watch and maybe start to imitate you. Did you sing?"

"Yes, they liked that. Also they began whispering their prayers as the girls and I said ours. So perhaps we did make a little start. I'm sure I will enjoy doing this and they were really friendly when they found we were planning to stay every night with them."

"I'm glad it worked well for you. I'll confess I missed you this morning. My girls are so little and you're nice to work with. But if you can help these poor savages to become more civilized, you will be of more use than helping me cook."

Feliciana and the girls ate noon meals and suppers with the Picos and then returned to the nunnery. From then on they were careful to wash their hands and faces each day, and brush their hair as the Indians watched. One day Feliciana noticed one of the girls had a large dried thistle she was trying to pull through her hair. She smiled at the girl and pretended to take no more notice. Another day more girls had thistles. Then one of the younger ones came to Feliciana shyly and held out the thistle to her and indicated she would like the older woman to help her.

Gently, Feliciana worked at the coarse straight black

hair. Soon it lay in a long smooth flow, but it still was greasy and dirty. Feliciana sighed. One thing at a time, she reminded herself.

Juan López stopped by the Picos' camp after supper the first few evenings. He seemed anxious at first, afraid the Indian girls would resent the newcomers.

"How does it really go?" he asked Feliciana after a few nights. "Are they accepting you?"

"They are dears, just like Spanish girls. They are curious about us, of course. But they laugh easily and like it when I sing. I even combed one girl's hair today."

Juan López whistled. "That will be something when they are all combed and clean of their own doing. And you—are you willing to go on with them until your *capitán* returns? Here, I brought these for the nunnery," he handed her a bunch of early wildflowers. "Perhaps these will brighten up the room a bit," he added, suddenly shy and leaving quickly.

As Feliciana looked for a clay bowl to put the flowers in, she wondered again about this man. He was thoughtful and gentle. Was there a reason why? Mostly these frontier soldiers were too busy shepherding their Indian charges around to show much inclination towards kind, helpful ways. Her heart skipped a beat. Had Juan López done these things for the nunnery before she came? No matter. She knew Muños, for all his wanting her for a wife, would never treat her or any woman as this soldier did. She hugged the thought to herself that she would be seeing him often in the next few days and, she hoped, weeks.

One sunny afternoon Feliciana sat outside the nunnery door, mending one of Tomasa's shifts and letting her mind wander to Juan López. She hadn't come in contact with many of the other soldiers here, and maybe that was why she was so constantly day-dreaming about him.

She was startled when Paula, one of the Indian girls, came and sat beside her.

In halting Spanish Paula said, "You make?"

"*Sí.* I make all of our clothes."

Paula reached for the needle and felt it carefully. "So

sharp." She took from a small pouch a needle made of bone. "Too hard to—" and Paula pantomimed putting the needle in and out of her skirt.

The clothes Paula wore were made from rough woven cotton. They were snagged and torn from the hard wear in the mission gardens.

Feliciana finished her needlefull of thread and then rethreaded it. There was a long tear near the hem of Paula's skirt and Feliciana quickly mended it.

"*Muchas gracias, Señora,*" Paula exclaimed. "You teach me? Use good needle?"

"Of course. I would like to. Are there any other girls who would like to learn to sew also?"

"Oh *sí*. We have no one to teach us except Indian way. *Padre* Paterna—oh no!" Paula giggled and giggled.

Feliciana had to laugh too, imagining the shy *padre* trying to teach the girls anything except religion. It had been only yesterday that Juan López had brought the blushing *padre* to her and explained the *padre* would like it if the young *señora* would mend his habit. Gravely she had assured him it would be no problem. When it was finished she gave it to the soldier to return.

Feliciana thought the mission *padres* had been sent out far from civilization unprepared for everyday living. It was good that now the government was sending women with their soldier husbands. Perhaps these women could make life easier for the *padres* too, by teaching domestic skills to the Indian girls, as she was trying to do.

After Paula left, Feliciana finished her own mending while she thought of the changes in the past few weeks. Every day they wondered when Anza would return. Now she knew that she would not be going north with him. She had her own home here with the Indian girls, although it probably was only a temporary one. Besides—she blushed as she thought of it—Juan López would be here.

In any case it would be weeks before Anza would be back from Monterey. She would give her few supplies left to the Picos. She had not told them of her decision yet. Perhaps now would be a good time to do that, and see if Jacinta approved.

Late that afternoon she joined the others at the Picos'

camp. The girls had been playing there all day with the other children. There had been much rain in the past few days and the worn tent had begun leaking. A damp wool smell filled the room. Smoke from the fire outside drifted in. Several girls were huddled in a corner playing with Gertrudis's half-grown kittens.

Doña Jacinta appeared glad to have company, and the two women settled themselves in another dry corner to visit. Feliciana saw that this was a good time to ask Jacinta's opinion.

CHAPTER 27

I've noticed the Indian girls are looking a little neater these days," said Jacinta. "They must be watching you."

"They are dears," Feliciana said. "They are even trying to comb their hair with large dry thistles. I wish I had combs and brushes for each of them. Just today one of the girls asked me to teach her to sew. But Jacinta, I have something I want to discuss with you. I've not said anything to my girls about this, but please tell me what you think.

"I've been looking ahead to when we come to the new place. I would have cattle and land to care for. I have no man, though I might be able to hire one. This is what I've about decided: I think I should stay here until Anza returns from San Francisco Bay and return with him to Sonora."

Jacinta said nothing as she poured some parched corn out to be pounded. Finally she said, "I too have wondered what you were planning to do. You know we would be happy to have you stay near us. But I'm not sure we are going to remain in the north either. My husband keeps hearing how cold it is there and says perhaps we will move back down here later. Now, if you had an understanding with *Don* Muños, that might be different."

Feliciana shook her head vigorously. "I wouldn't marry him if he was the only man around."

"Could you stay here at the mission until the *capitán* returns? I've noticed this soldier helping you. He seems a pleasant person. We think he's taken a liking to you," Jacinta gently teased, seeing Feliciana blush.

"Yes, I think I could stay here. The Indian girls like me

and there is much I could do to help them. I'm sure *Padre* Paterna would be willing. He is so bashful he can hardly look at the girls when he is teaching them their catechism. As for eating with them, that doesn't bother me. *Padre* Garcés has lived for many years eating with the Indians, and this food is much better."

"You can never tell what will happen next, so don't be in a hurry to decide. I'm sure you have more time to think about it before Anza returns." Jacinta gave Feliciana a warm hug.

That same evening Lieutenant Moraga and *Padre* Paterna asked the men of the expedition to meet with them. Afterwards *Señor* Pico reported to the family:

"*Padre* Paterna is getting anxious. He didn't think the soldiers would be gone so long. No new supplies have come to the mission and his warehouse is almost empty. Rats and mice have been multiplying and spoiling much of the grain. I told him we could cut back on our rations—couldn't we?"

Feliciana and the others agreed they could, and Pico went on: "He has sent a messenger to San Diego urging the *capitán* to return immediately."

"That means we should be getting ourselves ready to move on," said his wife. "It must be almost six weeks we have been here."

The colonists conferred and counted their supplies of grain, chocolate and other staples.

Feliciana approached Jacinta. "We have been eating with you—please take whatever is left of my supplies," she said. "We will be eating with the Indian girls all the time. And by the way," she went on, "there are many kinds of greens along the stream banks—parsnips and watercress especially."

"I haven't been out walking much because of the little girls, and also I'm not comfortable with so many Indians around," Jacinta confessed. "But I'll send the boys for some. More greens should help while we are here."

Several of the men offered to go into the nearby hills for game. Also they knew that Anza had warned the missions where they would stop to please have supplies for the colonists.

Juan López appeared at the end of the discussion to walk Feliciana and the girls back to the nunnery. Tonight he had a candle holder for her to put in the building.

"It was made in the pottery shed," he said. "They had some extras and I thought you might like more light in there. Also, here are some more candles."

"You are always thoughtful, *Señor*," said Feliciana. "That woven piece you brought a few nights ago is now hanging on the wall. The girls love its colors, and wanted me to thank you."

"There is something else I would like to say, *Señora*, if I may?" He looked anxiously at her, just like a small boy about to ask a favor, she thought.

"Of course," she replied, wondering if he too needed some mending done. Feliciana turned to the two girls and said, "Run along to bed. I will be in shortly."

Juan López looked uncomfortable. He paused so long, Feliciana thought he had forgotten what he had started to say.

"Please, *Señora*, I shouldn't even be mentioning this, but *Padre* Paterna asked me to ask you. Do you have to go on with *Capitán* Anza? Are you bound by some papers or money or such?"

"No," she replied, puzzled.

"It's this, *Señora*. We have never, or rather, he has never had a Spanish woman here to help with the Indian girls. He likes what you have been doing,. In—in other words, could you stay here and not go on with the others?" The soldier got this out with a rush and much blushing.

"Don't answer tonight, *Señora*. Think about it, but we want you to stay here."

Feliciana gazed at him with astonishment. Was he speaking just for *Padre* Paterna, or was he asking also for himself? Incredibly, it was the answer to her present problems. She replied with no hesitation:

"*Sí Señor*, I would like to stay on, but first I must think about it. I'm glad if I've been of some help, but to stay on—I must talk with my girls. Thank you, *Señor* for the chance to do something in exchange for what the mission is giving us. And I do want you to know how I appreciate your attention and the little gifts."

"I have some time free tomorrow. Perhaps you would like to ride around our lands here. If it doesn't rain we might go as far as the hills. It is beautiful country."

Feliciana laughed. "There was a time a few weeks ago I wouldn't have wanted to go for another ride. Now it sounds wonderful." To herself she added, "especially in such good company!" but aloud she only remarked, "Gallardo needs the exercise too."

"Bring the girls along if you wish," he suggested.

"*Gracias.* I think they'll like that. Every day we have gone to see Gallardo and he whinnies and asks when can he go for a run again. *Sí*, we shall be ready whenever you are." She watched *Señor* López go off to his evening duties, a warm glow in her heart. He wanted her to stay here!

As she turned to go into the nunnery she heard a loud crashing and much yelling. It came from the other side of the misson where the stores were kept.

She didn't dare leave the girls, so she stood, frightened and wary, in the doorway. Were unfriendly Indians attacking the mission?

It was not quite dark and she saw many of the colonists running toward the noise. There were loud and angry voices, followed by a quiet one she recognized as *Padre* Paterna's. Then there was more noise and angry voices again.

It seemed ages to Feliciana before *Señor* Pico came by to explain.

"Not all of those on the expedition were happy to cut their rations," he said. "They wouldn't listen to *Padre* Paterna and insisted the warehouse was full. Finally, Lieutenant Moraga pushed the *padre* aside and stood against the door.

"Mostly the angry men were *vaqueros* and muleteers. He ordered them back to their camps. I didn't know he could show so much authority, as he is always soft-spoken. No wonder Anza trusts him."

"Anyhow, Moraga said our large group of people with our food had attracted even more rats to the area. Again, *Padre* Paterna mentioned the rats eating the grain. He says he has asked twice for a ship to bring him a cat or two, but none have come so far."

Feliciana thought of Gertrudis's cat. Maybe she would share a kitten. But of course that was none of her business, Feliciana realized.

Pico was going on: "Then suddenly there was that little Peralta girl, Gertrudis, with her cage of mother cat and kittens. Her father went with Anza, you know, so there she was, handing that cage to Paterna with the tears running down her cheeks. That really shamed those men."

"Oh, the sweet child," Feliciana exclaimed. "She has loved and cared for those cats all the way, even keeping them under her blanket when it was so cold. That must have been hard for her to give them away."

"I understand Paterna gave her back two kittens. Anyway, I thought you'd be worried by all the noise and banging and loud voices."

"I was. *Muchas gracias* for stopping by."

As Feliciana went in, Tomasa appeared at her side. "I heard, *Mamá*. Gertrudis just loves those cats. She wouldn't hardly let anyone else touch them. I'm glad she gets to keep two. Maybe someday I can have a kitten," she added wistfully.

"Who knows?" Feliciana put her arm around Tomasa. "Who knows what will happen next?"

Inside she explained some of the noise to the frightened Indian girls and soon all was calm again.

"If tomorrow is pleasant would you like to go for a ride with *Señor* López and me?"

"Oh yes," said Tomasa eagerly.

"Me too?" asked Eustaquía, rubbing sleepy eyes.

"Yes, all of us. Now to bed and sleep everyone." A ride with *Señor* López—she called him Juan to herself—and Feliciana slept happily that night.

CHAPTER 28

The next day was glorious with the sun making the bright green grass glisten with dew. Gallardo nickered happily when Miguel, the stable boy, brought him out, ready to ride. He had thoroughly recovered from the long trip and his coat was sleek and shiny.

López started to lift Tomasa onto the horse when he asked her, "Would you like to ride with me, *niñita*? You may sit in front and see more."

"*Sí, gracias*," she said with no hesitation.

Her mother looked at her in surprise, but said nothing.

"Me too," cried Eustaquía.

"Me too," Feliciana echoed the four-year-old and laughed.

"Next time, *niñita*—OK?" asked the soldier.

"No, now." Eustaquía started to pout. She was still pouting when López put her on Gallardo with her mother. Feliciana was curious how he was going to solve the problem. He just smiled calmly at the child.

"Supposing Tomasa rides half way with me and then we'll trade and you can ride back. And next," he paused with a mischievous glance at Feliciana, "your *mamá* can ride with me."

Feliciana looked at his dancing eyes and felt a sudden thrill. Would he dare?

"*Mamá!*" exclaimed Tomasa.

"*Mamá?*" echoed Eustaquía.

"Sure," said López. "I can't take all three of you at once or my poor horse would fall down."

The girls looked at their mother's startled face and they all laughed together, Eustaquía forgetting her pout.

As they set off on a path that led towards the hills, he said casually across to Feliciana, "*Señora*, out here we don't stand on ceremony. Please, just call me Juan."

"*Gracias*, Juan, and I will feel more comfortable if you call me Feliciana."

As they rode side by side, Feliciana's heart was pounding so hard she was sure Juan could hear it. Was he feeling in a special mood today? His merry eyes showed another side of him she hadn't seen before. Always he had been quiet, gentle, considerate and sometimes shy. But this was a different Juan today—an irresistible Juan.

As though nothing was changed, Juan showed them the fields of wild flowers that were springing up everywhere: red and yellow paint brush, blue iris, and lupine.

"Listen, girls," said Feliciana, "can you hear the birds singing? And doesn't it smell like spring? Oh, I like California, if this is a sample."

"There are lots more trees here than in *Abuelas's* garden," put in Tomasa. "Now I'm glad we came. Is it all like this?" she asked Juan.

"No," Juan admitted. "Remember you had snow when you first rode into California? But this is the best place, I think."

He pointed out the fat cattle in the fields. "These came with Rivera and Portolá up through Baja. There was so little food that most of them died on the way. But you see how well they are doing here now.

"The milk in your morning chocolate, *niñitas*, comes from these. That same milk makes good butter and cheese."

"Somebody talked about California money the other day," said Feliciana. "It sounded like they were talking about the cattle. How is that?"

Juan explained. "When they are killed for meat, then the hide is carefully dried. These are worth much money to Spain. All our candles are made from the fat—we even can send some on the ships. These hides are our money."

Feliciana hardly took in all Juan was saying. How could he be so matter-of-fact when she still had trouble controlling her voice? His teasing eyes hadn't changed, though, when he turned to look at her. She almost missed the sheep until Tomasa spoke:

144

"Look at the little lambs. Aren't they cute?"

"Cute, *Mamá*, cute. Can I hold one?"

Juan laughed. "I don't think his *mamá* would like that, Eustaquía."

"My *mamá* wouldn't like some people to hold me, either," she said.

"I know I don't want that *Señor* Muños to ever hold me again," Tomasa said emphatically.

Feliciana was jolted. Had Juan heard about Muños's attention to her and the girls before this?

"What about me?" asked Juan quietly.

"You're different. Eustaquía and I like you," said Tomasa, and her sister nodded in agreement. Me too, thought their mother.

They watched the sheep for a few minutes. Juan broke the silence. "Our grass is so rich here, we can raise both cattle and sheep. These are not the merinos of Spain, but they do produce warm blankets and *serapes*."

"At home our land was too poor to even feed a few sheep," Feliciana said. "But with so much water you seem to be able to grow most everything."

"We do have our dry period each summer, you know," he reminded her. "We have developed irrigation ditches from the San Gabriel Wash to bring water to our gardens.

"Here's about as far as we should go. Let's change riders here and then let the horses run a bit."

Tomasa slid off quickly and Eustaquía beamed all over as Juan lifted her onto his horse. Juan whispered something in Tomasa's ear before he helped her onto Gallardo.

"Want to go fast?" he asked Eustaquía. "I'll hang on to you tight. OK, Feliciana?" She nodded wordlessly. The girls loved to ride fast.

"Yes, fast, fast!" cried Eustaquía. Nobody mentioned a time when Tomasa wasn't held onto at the river. Feliciana was grateful—the least said about Muños the better.

Gallardo was more than ready. López's strong little mustang gave Gallardo a good race, but the big chestnut's legs were longer. Eustaquía looked more than satisfied with her ride and she gave Juan a hug as he put her down.

Feliciana was surprised that Tomasa had not jumped off, but waited to be helped. Then, before Feliciana could move, Juan had helped Tomasa down and then leaped

145

behind her on Gallardo. The girls laughed and clapped. "Now it's *Mamá's* turn," Tomasa cried.

"Stay back by the stables, girls," Juan called. "We will be right back."

Feliciana, riding side saddle, felt helpless as Juan took the reins in one hand and put his other arm around her. Gallardo took off at a slap of the reins, and Feliciana was held tight against Juan.

She had a flicker of anger until Juan brushed her hair with his cheek and said, "I'll let you down in a moment. I've wanted to do this for a long time. Please forgive me. Next time I will ask."

Feliciana said nothing but pressed against him, feeling shameless and wishing the ride would never end.

As they came back to the girls she looked around to see if anyone was looking. Then suddenly she didn't care if anybody *had* seen them. He was off the horse in a flash and helped her down. He gave her a long adoring look and went quickly off to his job.

While Feliciana brushed down Gallardo, the girls ran off to the Picos to wait for dinner. She wondered what they would tell about the ride. Not much, she imagined. They were glad to get back to the kittens.

"Gallardo, Gallardo," she murmured. "I think I'm falling in love, and I think he likes me. But two months is a short time to learn to know someone new. I must wait. I'll have time to see him often while I stay here until Anza returns."

After supper she took the girls for a little walk. "Tomasa, suppose I told you I was thinking of staying here until *el Capitán* returns from San Francisco Bay—how would you feel?"

Tomasa was puzzled. "You mean stay here alone? Why can't we go with *Señor* Pico and all our friends? Don't they want us with them anymore?"

"No, it's not that, *niñita*. They want us—but *querida mía*, what could I do when we came to that new land? Each family would have his own place. I can't build a house or make a garden unless I pay someone to do it, and I have no money."

"Then why did we come, *Mamá? Abuela* wanted us to stay with her. You said we could have a new place together," Tomasa reminded her.

"But then I didn't know how hard it was going to be. *Sí*, we can go on if I agree to marry *Don* Muños."

"Oh no, *Mamá!* Please don't do that." Tomasa would never forget that day she was thrown into the Colorado River. *Don* Muños had told her he was sorry and then added, "But if you had held on tight you wouldn't have fallen."

"No, *Mamá*. I don't want him for a *papá*, and I know Eustaquía doesn't either, do you Eustaquía?" Her sister shook her head.

"Neither do I, *niñitas*." Feliciana gave the girls a big hug. "*Padre* Paterna and *Señor* López have asked me to stay here and help with the young Indian girls, just like I've been doing. I'm sure you could find some little Indian girls to play with."

"And when *Capitán* Anza comes back we have to ride all that way home again?"

Feliciana sighed. "I don't know, Tomasa. We'll wait and see. I like helping these people, and I'm willing to work here too."

"If we stayed here, *Mamá*, I could play with the kittens Gertrudis gave to *Padre* Paterna. They're used to me and Eustaquía, and it would feel a little bit like home . . . " Tomasa's voice trailed off.

Feliciana held her close. It was so much to ask of the little girls, she thought. And all because she had been so stubborn.

That day when they had looked down from the snow into the sun-filled valley she had felt she was right in coming—and that there was a miracle waiting here for her in the new land. Now she wondered what it might be. Could it possibly be Juan? The girls had liked him immediately.

They finished the walk home in silence, each thinking her own thoughts.

Before dawn the next morning Feliciana wakened to hear loud angry voices. It wasn't until after breakfast that she learned that twenty-five of the best horses had been stolen from the corral by five muleteers.

Señor Pico said they were some of the men who had

tried to break down the granary doors. Lieutenant Moraga had left immediately to capture the men and animals. Feliciana's heart nearly broke when she learned Gallardo had been one of those stolen. Now what would she do?

When Tomasa and Eustaquía realized their beloved horse was gone they sobbed and sobbed. Feliciana could do little to comfort them. Now I will have to stay, she thought. At least Juan will be here—she hardly dared dream about what might be.

A messenger arrived the next day saying Anza was on his way and would be here tomorrow.

Juan came to see Feliciana. "I'm so sorry about your horse. I know how much he meant to you and the girls. Come out with me for a few minutes."

They walked towards the *corral* where the men were strengthening the fence and bars.

"He was my husband's horse, Juan. When José was killed his *capitán* gave him to me. Gallardo carried us safely all the way—across the desert, the rivers and over the mountains."

They stood looking at the remaining horses. "If you see one that you would like, *Padre* Paterna wants you to have it."

"*Gracias*, Juan, but I doubt if I'll have need of a horse. I'm sure now that we will stay here at least until Anza returns."

"You mean it, Feliciana? And maybe you might stay here even after Anza goes back to Mexico City?" He took her hand in both of his.

"I haven't decided that yet," she answered quickly. "I can see now that I have no business going to San Francisco Bay. I have no one to help me build a house or care for the animals we have been promised. I'm waiting to see *el Capitán*, and then I'll decide."

"I know what *Padre* Paterna and I both wish, Feliciana. For me, I hope you never return to your old home." Juan blushed hotly at this bold declaration.

Feliciana said no more as they walked back to the nunnery, but she didn't withdraw her hand. All at once her heart and mind were at peace, but she was too shy to say that now she *was* home—her new home, at least wherever Juan would be.

CHAPTER 29

Two days later Feliciana saw Anza and his men ride into San Gabriel. He shook his head when someone asked if he was bringing supplies.

"No," said Anza bitterly. "*Comandante* Rivera decided San Diego was more important than sending supplies to the other missions."

Feliciana thought it was not an auspicious time to tell him of the problems of the last few days. But some of the colonists were so upset that they immediately told him of the rioting over the cut in rations, and the missing horses.

Feliciana felt sorry for Anza, who was first disturbed and then furious when he learned of the theft of the horses. Sergeant Grijalva eased Anza a little, telling how Moraga had already gone after the five muleteers involved. "They were the same ones who have caused trouble all along the way," he said.

"Let me rest and think this over," Anza told the people.

He was tired when he had arrived, and now Feliciana saw he was deeply depressed. He needed time to recover from this blow. She watched Paterna take Anza into his own quarters while a special welcome-home feast was being prepared.

Anza spoke to them after a bountiful meal of mutton and beef stews. "If you will get yourselves ready, we will be on our way in two days. We'll manage it somehow, and," with a wry smile, "I'd like to stay a few miles ahead of that *comandante*."

There were cheers from the colonists, anxious to be on the way. Feliciana wondered if they had enough horses when someone asked, "Can we manage without the horses those wretches stole?"

"*Padre* Paterna has offered any we need. I'll leave Corporal Peralta in charge until Moraga returns. Some of those who went to San Diego with me may stay and rest if they wish. Then they will all follow us with the cattle. We will wait in Monterey."

Feliciana thought how nice it was for her girls. *Señora* Peralta was staying to let her husband get some rest. The Alvisos, Grijalvas and Peraltas had girls Tomasa's age.

Tomasa nudged her mother. "Gertrudis is staying and we can see the kittens. It's all right, *Mamá*. We'll stay here."

Of course there was more news at supper. Feliciana was fascinated at how these tales were spread. It seems *Padre* Font told some of the people that Rivera had tried to talk Font into staying in San Diego. Rivera became angry when Font insisted he had been told by the viceroy to stay with Anza all the way to the new *pueblo*.

Feliciana remembered how Font had ridden right behind Anza since leaving Horcasistas, apparently taking Bucareli's order seriously.

Later *Padre* Font stopped at the Picos' camp. Feliciana heard him chuckle and say, "I don't think Rivera likes Anza taking the colonists to San Francisco Bay instead of him. We had just decided to come back anyway when the messenger arrived. We didn't ask Rivera's permission to leave. And here we are."

As she and Juan headed towards the nunnery that night, Feliciana caught her first sight of Muños since his return. He looked no happier than he had before, and she hastily glanced away. Now she was glad she had decided to stay on at the mission. She hoped Muños wasn't one of those Anza was leaving behind with Peralta.

"Run on into bed, girls, " Feliciana said. "I'll soon be in."

"And now that *el Capitán* has returned, are you still willing to remain when he goes on?"

"*Sí*, more than ever, Juan. I'll miss my friends, but there is no future in the north for me. I can't start a home nor care for cattle and sheep. Probably I should never have come. Tomorrow I shall tell Anza that I will stay here until he returns. He is a wonderful man."

Feliciana realized she was just talking to cover up her embarrassment with Juan since the horseback ride. She lapsed into silence.

Juan broke it, taking her hands in his. "Aren't there any compensations here?" he asked. "Let's walk around the nunnery for a little while. No one will bother the girls."

"For a little while," Feliciana agreed, her heart pounding. Still holding hands, they walked silently. Twice Feliciana thought Juan was going to speak, but didn't. She thought she saw a figure in the background but paid no heed. Maybe Juan wanted to be sure no one saw them.

Suddenly Juan made up his mind. He turned to face her. "I don't want to press you, Feliciana, but it's not just *Padre* Paterna who wants you here, but I do. *Querida*, I wanted to let you know when we were on Gallardo how I wanted to hold you and have you with me forever."

As he pulled her to him she realized it was what she would like too. "Feliciana, *querida*, I've been hoping you would stay because of me. Perhaps in time you would be willing to marry me."

"Oh Juan, but I can't answer that tonight. I must talk to Anza first—but I will be here, and we'll see each other every day, and—" Feliciana blushed and pushed him away as she fled to the nunnery, her mind in a whirl.

The next day Feliciana asked *Señor* Pico to find Anza for her. She had slept little the night before—all she could think of was Juan's arms around her and his voice saying he wanted to marry her.

Anza came in the early afternoon. "It's good to see you so well, *Señora*," he greeted her. "*Padre* Paterna tells me you have been helping here with the Indian girls. That's wonderful. And now you have something to tell me?"

"*Sí, Capitán* Anza. I know that my husband and I signed to go to San Francisco Bay. Now that I'm alone I'm not sure that I could make a place by myself in this new land. I don't want to ask others to do my work. Would it be all right with you if I should stay here until you return and

151

then go back with you to Sonora? *Padre* Paterna said I might stay with the Indian girls and help teach them. That way I would be earning my way."

"*Sí, Señora* Arballo. I heard something of this from the good *padre*. I understand your feelings. I had hoped you might find one of our bachelors congenial, but I guess that is not to be. No, my dear, you are not bound in any way to continue.

"As you know, I'm leaving some of the colonists here for a few days and they will follow with the cattle. If you should change your mind we'd be most happy to see you. At any rate I shall be back here in a short time and see what your wishes are then."

Feliciana thanked him, relieved he had understood. But then he had always understood his people, hadn't he. Those warm brown eyes seemed to look into your very mind.

In a flash Feliciana realized Juan had that same kind of eyes. Would he too always understand her point of view? She blushed hotly as Juan came by just then. Could he have read her mind? Absurd, she reassured herself. He had come to tell her Paula was looking for her.

"Oh yes," she said. "I promised to find some needles and help the girls with their sewing."

Feliciana hurried to the Picos' tent, where she had asked Jacinta to keep a little packet of needles she had wheedled from the other women. They were precious because no one knew when replacements would come. The women had been generous, even giving her some of their extra cloth for Feliciana to use in making shifts for the Indian girls.

Paterna had told her he would release a few of them at a time to her sewing class. The afternoon slipped by in happy companionship with the girls. When she came out of the nunnery to go to supper, *Don* Muños was waiting for her, the now perpetual scowl on his face.

"What are you doing in that hovel?" he asked. "I've been waiting a long time to talk to you."

"I'm sorry you had to wait—I didn't know you were here," she said cooly. "I'm teaching the girls to sew, among other things. Tomasa and Eustaquía and I have moved in here to sleep," she added. "It is no hovel, but a warm place to be when it rains. We are grateful to *Padre* Paterna for thinking of us."

"Or was it that soldier who wants you to himself?" he sneered. "Are you packed? We leave in the morning, you know."

"I am not going with Anza. I've spoken to him and he understands my reasons. I'm staying here until he returns and then I'll probably go back to Sonora. I'm sure, though," Feliciana added coldly, "that is of no interest to you."

"I am interested, *Señora*. You encouraged me all the way here. You were tired and ill when you told me to leave you alone. You just need a strong hand and firm orders and you will make a fine wife for me."

"Leave me alone, *Señor* Muños," Feliciana cried as he reached out and grabbed her. Ignoring her protests, he held her firmly and kissed her.

She struggled and tried to call out, but his hard mouth smothered hers. She kicked him viciously in the shins.

"You little wildcat," he exclaimed, and seizing her by the shoulders shook her repeatedly. "That is what I want in a wife," he laughed brutally. "I want a wife I must tame, not some cringing creature."

Feliciana had screamed when he shook her. Juan and *Padre* Font rushed out of the nearby mission. Juan swiftly grabbed one of Muños's arms and thrust him away from Feliciana. Gently, he took her in his arms just as Font arrived, hampered by his long robe.

The *padre* remonstrated firmly. "She needs a man no doubt, but not an animal trainer."

Señor Muños, apparently stunned by the sudden attack, physical and vocal, stalked off, glaring at all three.

Feliciana, furious at Muños, humiliated by Font's remarks, and mortified to have Juan see her in such a setting, wanted only to get away from them all.

Juan was not to be put off. Firmly but tenderly he held her as Font asked her kindly, "Are you all right, *Señora?* May I apologize for some of my past remarks? Muños is indeed not good husband material. We shall see that he goes north with us. *Buenas noches*, and may your life here be more peaceful."

Feliciana saw him give Juan an appraising look, nod approval, and return to the mission.

"So that is the Muños Tomasa disapproved of," Juan said. "If Font hadn't been here I would have beaten the man. I still will, if you wish."

She clung briefly to Juan and then stepped back. "Thank you for coming so quickly. No, don't fight with him, I have caused enough trouble. I just want to keep out of his sight."

Juan walked her back to the nunnery door. "Is it safe to leave you, *mi querida?* There is no one else about to rush in and grab you?" he added, trying to get a smile.

Feliciana was in no mood for joking, but gave him a slight squeeze of his hand. Juan kissed her softly on her cheek.

"Don't let this disturb you—I will be on watch. Now sleep well. Tomorrow he will be gone and out of your life."

In bed that night, Feliciana, sleepless, relived that scene with Muños. How dared he intrude in her life again? What must Juan be thinking? Life had been so peaceful with him, but now—would he ever want to see her again? If she could stay out of sight of Muños until Anza and the colonists had gone, could she possibly make Juan understand? Had her chances for a happy future been ruined by Muños? Could anything else come between Juan and herself? Softly she sobbed herself to sleep.

CHAPTER 30

In the daylight the next morning Feliciana wondered and hoped she had underestimated Juan's understanding and caring for her. At least she would soon know as she joined the families who were staying behind.

It was Wednesday, February 21, and they were loading the old gray tents onto the mules and organizing the train. Compared to five months ago, the operation proceeded with no wasted effort.

Padre Font held a longer than usual mass and reminded them of all the hardships they had endured. It was 11:30 before his lengthy prayer was concluded.

As Feliciana was standing with the Alviso and Peralta families, Juan came up beside her. Softly he said to her, "I'll be most happy when they are all gone and you are here with me at the mission alone."

Her heart leaped. He still wanted her. Teasingly, she reminded him there was time to change her mind.

"But you won't, will you?" He turned a worried face towards her, putting his hand on her arm.

Señora Peralta gave a small scream as a horse and rider raced towards them. *Señor* Munos leaped from his saddle and rushed at Juan with a knife in his hand. Juan pushed Feliciana aside and sidestepped the angry soldier, the knife grazing Juan's sleeve.

"That is my woman!" shouted Munos. "Take your hand from her!"

"I am not your woman," Feliciana cried as Juan pushed her behind him and said, "This is between Munos and me, *querida*. Stay back."

155

"If I can't have her no one else shall," Muños shouted, swinging the knife up again and lunging at the unarmed Juan. A furious Anza seized Muños's arm from behind.

"Sheath that knife or I'll have you in jail. What *is* this fight about?"

"*Capitán* Anza," said Feliciana, stepping from behind Juan, who took her hand. "*Señor* Muños has been trying to force me to accompany you north. Please tell him I am not continuing."

"You heard the *señora*. She is correct. She informed me yesterday that she would stay here until I return from San Francisco Bay. She is free to make her own choice."

"*Capitán*, you have been most patient with me. Now I have definitely made up my mind, thanks to *Señor* Muños." Feliciana sent the latter a mocking smile. Turning to Juan and giving him a radiant smile, she took his arm and said, "I have decided to stay at Mission San Gabriel. I am going to marry *Señor* Juan López."

Juan's face lit up with joy—barely able to control himself, he heard a familiar voice speak: "Amen. The *señora* has at last become reasonable. All young women need a man to guide them." Juan and Felician exchanged amused looks as Font moved on.

A smiling Paterna came forward to wish them much happiness and a good marriage. No one paid any attention to the angry, scowling Muños as he mounted his horse and viciously spurred it to his place in line.

Anza spoke. "Again, I congratulate you on your good judgment, *Señora*. I'm especially happy and looking forward to seeing you on my return. And congratulations to you, López. You have a courageous, intelligent and delightful young woman."

The two men exchanged salutes. As Anza rode off he turned and said with a mischievous smile, "Do ask her to dance the *fandango* for you, López."

Juan was speechless and dazed with happiness. He held Feliciana closely in his arms as the travelers prepared to leave. She watched the familiar routine with no regrets.

Padre Font raised the banner high, the horn blew, the mission bells rang and, chanting the *Alabado*, the colonists moved on. Tomasa and Eustaquía waved to their friends. They were glad now to be staying here, though probably they would never see them again.

Francisca Peralta and her husband turned to the young couple, congratulating them and giving them their blessing, before Corporal Peralta went off to check on the cattle and *vaqueros*, his responsibility until Moraga returned.

"My Gertrudis is so happy to have your girls staying. She knows they love the kittens. She cried half the night, though she wanted *Padre* Paterna to have them. Like giving your own children away, I guess."

"Tomasa is happy too that all her friends aren't leaving at once. It's worked out nicely for the children."

"I don't know how long we will stay," *Señora* Peralta said. "Two of our boys are helping with the cattle. It all depends on Moraga. May I come over and see where you are staying?"

Juan could hardly tear himself away from Feliciana. He had work to do and told her he would see her later. Apparently his mind still was reeling with her unexpected announcement.

The two women went into the nunnery. "Why, how clean it is," exclaimed *Doña* Francisca. "I never dreamed the building for the Indian girls could be so pleasant and attractive."

She approved of the small brooms they had made from rushes. More cots had been added and most of the girls now had their own beds, topped by neatly folded blankets. In one corner, on a rudely finished table, were the sewing supplies.

"I am helping the girls make shifts to sleep in. They appreciate the material you women gave them. They love the feel of the fine cloth next to their skins. They try very hard to please.

"The girls and I will now take our meals with them. They watch Tomasa and Eustaquía to see how they handle their food." Feliciana laughed. "It's good for my girls too. They have to be on their best behavior."

"I heard Eustaquía thought it would be fun to be an Indian girl—not have to wash her face or comb her hair."

157

The two women had a good laugh over that. "Just two days and Eustaquía wanted hers brushed again. Hers tangles easily."

"Will you continue helping the Indian girls after you are married?"

"I haven't thought about that," confessed Feliciana. "So much has happened suddenly—not going north with Anza and then deciding to marry Juan. But I imagine I will. He has his work and there is plenty here for me to do."

"I'm truly happy for you, *Doña* Feliciana. While I don't know your Juan López, I'm so glad you're not marrying that *Señor* Muños. He is a handsome man, but there is a wild brutal streak in him. You would never be happy with such a person. You would never please him with your sunny outgoing nature." *Señora* Peralta gave her a warm hug and said it was time she was on her way.

Feliciana moved in a pleasant daze. Her fears of the night before were gone. Juan truly was the most loving and understanding of men—at least of those she had known. She promised herself she would never let him down.

She was the center of attention wherever she went. When the Indian girls learned she was staying, they worked harder than ever to please her. They brought fresh wildflowers every day to brighten the nunnery.

Tomasa and Eustaquía too were in a happy world of their own. They had missed the near-tragedy, as they had gone to play with the almost-grown kittens. Mother cat was an excellent mouser, and the whole cat family was growing fatter.

Then one day during this waiting period a sentry shot a signal. Feliciana rushed out with the others, curious as to who was coming. It was not just a "someone," but a large group of horses being herded by Moraga and his *vaqueros*. The five thieves were tied to their horses and quickly transferred to the *carcel*.

The people gathered around Moraga, who Feliciana could see was jubilant, though tired and exhausted. He had not only brought back all the stolen horses, but had also found some of the cattle that had stampeded one night long ago on the trail. They let him go when he promised to tell them all about it after he had rested.

Later, refreshed and fed, Lieutenant Moraga stopped to chat with Feliciana. She thanked him for bringing Gallardo back.

"Your horse is a beautiful animal. They had gone a long way, *Señora*. They were almost to the lake where we were given fish. The thieves had lost their way though, and were heading into a boggy marshland. The whole group were in danger of floundering when we arrived and rescued the horses and thieves."

"What will happen to the muleteers?"

"They will be whipped and then held until Anza returns. They will be on short rations, but won't be injured." Moraga smiled at her concern, and again Feliciana noted the warmth that the leaders had shown.

She hurried to tell the girls that Gallardo was back. Now a new happy life was opening up to all of them.

CHAPTER 31

That evening Feliciana and the girls went for a short walk. It wasn't long before Juan joined them.

"Do you mind if I come too?" he asked. Tomasa reached for one hand and Eustaquía the other. Feliciana couldn't help thinking how like a family they were already as they walked towards the little stream that was starting to dry up. Singing frogs and other small night sounds were soft and peaceful.

Feliciana said nothing. She was so happy and in love, there was no need for small talk. Even the girls quit their chattering. A mockingbird sang a plaintive song to his mate in the far trees.

Juan, who also had been silent, stopped suddenly. Putting his hands on Feliciana's shoulders, he turned her to face him.

"*Querida mía*," he said, "I am going to forget what you told *Capitán* Anza this morning. Oh no," he added quickly, as he saw the shock in her eyes. "It's not that I don't want you for my wife, but you were pressured by the circumstances.

"You have said you needed more time to know your mind and I want you to take as long as you wish. I don't want to be the best way out of a desparate situation."

Feliciana put her hand across his mouth. "Hush. That was not a sudden decision because I was frightened. It was *Señor* Muños himself who decided me. Oh my dear one, when he rushed at you—then I knew I wanted to be with you for the rest of my life. If he had hurt you, I would never have forgiven him. But now I am grateful to him that it turned out as it did. He is gone from my life forever and I have you."

Juan still held her shoulders. "Are you really sure? You have no more hesitation?"

For answer, she slipped her arms around his neck. "I'm sure for all time. When we came for this walk and the girls each took your hand, I thought, 'Now we are a whole family again.' "

Juan held her close. "Oh *querida, querida,*" he murmured over and over, his lips on her hair.

There was a tug at Juan's leg. Eustaquía looked up at him with a worried face. "Are you going to be my real *papá,* or just a pertend one?"

Juan picked her up and held her close. "Your real one, I hope—if you want me."

Eustaquía burst into tears and threw her arms around his neck. "A real one, a real one," she sobbed over and over.

Feliciana and Juan exchanged glances. What had brought this on?

Tomasa took her mother's hand. "I never told you. I didn't want to worry you. Some of the big boys from Tubac were always teasing her that she never had a real *papá.* When she told them *Capitán* Anza was her pretend *papá,* they'd laugh and tell her that's all she would ever have."

"But why?" asked her mother. "Why should they be so mean? Did they say that to you, too?"

"Yes, but it didn't bother me. I remember my *papá* better than Eustaquía does. But when they would say things about—" Tomasa stopped, embarrassed.

"Yes, Tomasa? What else did they say?"

Tomasa hesitated and then said, "It was about you, *Mamá.* And they weren't true things either, *Mamá.*"

Feliciana was very quiet. "Like what, *niñita?*"

Tomasa was plainly distressed. "About how you danced and sang. But you are so beautiful when you dance, and everyone loved your singing, just like we do at night."

Juan squatted down beside Tomasa, Eustaquía on his knee. "Eustaquía, just as Tomasa says, you did have a real *papá.* He was a brave soldier and then he was killed. But you did have a real *papá.* I'll try to be a real one too. Your *mamá* is a very brave lady and those boys were just trying to make you cry. Some people are like that. But you and I

161

and all the people here at San Gabriel know and love your *mamá* very much.

"I think that's a long speech. It's time to go see *Padre* Paterna and ask him to set a date for me to marry your *mamá*. Then we shall be one very happy family, eh?"

Eustaquía hugged him closer as he rose. Then, with each holding one of Tomasa's hands, they started back to the mission.

Feliciana exchanged looks with Juan over Tomasa's head. What a burden the little girls had been carrying. Feliciana felt her face flaming with the insults the boys must have flung at the two children. She remembered the first *fiesta* in Tubac when she had danced the *fandango*. Had those boys overheard *Don* Muños's remarks to her?

"Feliciana." She realized Juan was speaking to her. "What was it that Anza called back to me? Something about asking you to dance for me. Apparently he thought it was exceptional."

She looked up to see a teasing smile on Juan's face. And once again she knew this was the man for her. He wanted her for herself and had no criticism of anything in her past or outside their present life together.

Happiness overflowing, she returned the teasing smile. "You will just have to wait, *Señor*," she said.

With Eustaquía sing-songing, "I got a *papá*, I got a *papá*," and Tomasa skipping and swinging between their hands, Feliciana and Juan walked into the chapel in search of *Padre* Paterna.

Feliciana had seen much of the Alviso and Peralta families, and now she asked the two *señoras* to help her choose her wedding dress. Once again the little trunk with her special clothes was unpacked. At the bottom was her wedding dress from that time that seemed so long ago. Wordlessly she looked at it and then laid it aside. Someday it might do for Tomasa, but it had special memories. *Señora* Peralta picked up the yellow ruffled dress Feliciana had worn to the dance in Tubac.

"This, I think," she said. "You looked so beautiful in it. Now after a long rest, you are looking young and radiant again. At least this is my choice."

162

After looking at the few other things, Angela Alviso agreed. Feliciana had some second thoughts, but kept them to herself. No need to tell them about the boys who had been cruel to the little girls. Yes, the yellow dress it should be. Though everyone else on the expedition had seen it, Juan had not.

The ten families still in San Gabriel brought small gifts to Feliciana: a fan, a tortoise-shell comb, a bowl and other cooking needs.

"Where are you going to live?" Francisca Peralta asked her one day. Feliciana had laughed. "Everything has been so sudden we haven't talked about that."

"I've seen some little houses around here—maybe one of those," suggested Angela Alviso.

"I'll tell you when I know," Feliciana told them. One more thing to ask Juan about.

That evening after supper, Feliciana and Juan went walking. The girls were with Gertrudis and the cats. "We have never discussed where we are going to live," Feliciana said. "I'm sure you don't plan on me staying in the nunnery." She laughed at his reaction. "Have you planned where we'll stay?"

"That has been my secret, *querida*, until I was sure you were really staying. Come, I have time to show it to you."

At the end of the row of little *adobe* houses was one she hadn't noticed before. There were several Indian men working on the roof.

Juan stopped and asked, "How goes it?"

They grinned back at him. "*Bueno, Señor.* It will soon be ready."

"This, my love, is to be our house. As they said, it is almost finished. Just waiting for you to say what you want done inside," he added.

"It is just for us? It does not belong to the mission and loaned to us?"

"It's my house and I'm having it built. I have been a soldier for more than the ten years. Also I will be given any tools and animals that we might wish—a few chickens, a goat, perhaps."

"Oh Juan! You never mentioned this—I never dreamed—"

"I wanted it for a surprise. I was entitled to it, but I didn't know if I was ever going to have a wife—they are in short supply here," he added with a laugh. "When I saw you that day we took the horses to Anza, I knew I wanted you. At first I thought you had a husband and I was too late. Then I thought you were going to go on with the others. I was prepared to ask for a transfer to the *presidio* at Yerba Buena just to be near you."

"But Juan, I must have looked terrible when you came out on the trail. I was sick and I had fainted. How could you even look at me?"

"It was very, very easy, *querida*. Shall we look inside?"

There were two rooms. They still needed their walls whitewashed, but Feliciana could picture how she would like it.

"What can we do for furniture? Though we don't need much." Feliciana was overwhelmed suddenly with how little she was bringing to their new home—a few pans and the gifts of her friends.

"They will make it at the mission. You just tell us what you'd like."

"Oh Juan, this is a miracle." Her face lit up. "Out there on the gray snowy mountain top we looked down onto the valley where it was sunny and green. We called it the California miracle, and I wondered if maybe there might be a miracle here for me. Then I decided to go back to Sonora with Anza. You, Juan, are my California miracle, only I didn't recognize it until just now."

Juan gathered her into his arms and kissed her thoroughly, to the amusement of the watching Indians—but the two were unaware of anyone around them.

The bell rang for the evening meal and, as in a dream world, they returned to the others.

CHAPTER 32

How the time flew by. Together they talked to *Padre* Paterna about their needs for the little house. A date was set for the wedding before the colonists and cattle left for the north. The young Indian women appeared thrilled; even though Feliciana would no longer live in the nunnery, she promised to teach them evey day.

March arrived with a great splurge of new wildflowers. The workers were in the fields one day putting in the new crops when they heard a shout in the distance. Two men were approaching on foot. Then an answering shout went up and *Padre* Paterna rang the bell in welcome.

Feliciana, wondering who was coming, hurried out with the girls from the nunnery. As the figures came closer, she gave a glad cry and rushed to meet them.

"*Padre* Garcés! What are you doing here? I thought you had gone down the Colorado River."

It was indeed the popular *padre* of the expedition with his Indian friend. In turn he looked at Feliciana in amazement. "What are *you* doing here? I thought you were on your way to San Francisco Bay."

She laughed. "It's a long story, *Padre*. I'll tell you later. I know you want to see *Padre* Paterna."

It was the next day before Garcés had a chance to visit with Feliciana. She told him of her growing concern as to how she would manage alone in the new land; how she had decided to wait here for Anza's return and then go back to Sonora with him.

Padre Garcés's eyes twinkled. "And now there is another change of plans? Did I hear right? It looks like that charm must have been working."

165

She blushed. "Yes, *Padre*. Juan López and I are to be married soon and I will stay here. How did you know? Oh, *Padre* Paterna told you!"

"Yes, he told me. He also suggested I perform the ceremony since we had been together so long. This is Saturday, the second of March. I can only stay a short time—would next Wednesday, the sixth, be too soon?"

"I would love to have you, *Padre*. It would be like having part of my family with me. But Wednesday! That is so soon!" She thought a bit. "Yes, I would like that."

"And your young man? It will be all right with him?"

Happily and proudly Feliciana answered him, "Yes, I know it will be all right. But here he comes. You ask him."

Feliciana introduced Juan to *Padre* Garcés.

"*Señor* López, I congratulate you on your good fortune. She was a favorite of mine from Tubac to the Colorado. We tried to marry her off, but she was rather choosy. May I have the privilege of performing the ceremony? It will have to be soon, for I must be on my way again. I only came by to be sure the expedition had gone."

"*Padre* Garcés," said Juan, his face lighting up, "it can't be too soon for me. I have waited a long time for someone like her."

"Then let's find Paterna and make plans." And Garcés led the way to the *padre's* little room.

Saturday to Wednesday, Feliciana's mind was in a whirl. The thrilled Indian girls searched the fields and hillsides for the right flowers for the mission chapel.

Francisca Peralta and Angela Alviso washed Feliciana's clothes. They made up the new bed with the rope lacings and scoured the table and benches just finished in the shop.

Corporal Peralta came to see Feliciana. "*Doña* Feliciana, we would like to plan the *fiesta* for your wedding. It can't be the traditional three-day one, for we too are leaving next week. And one request, *por favor*—will you dance for us one last time?"

All these offerings overwhelmed her. They were acting as her family: caring for her clothes, giving her the wedding feast and dance. Soon they would ride out of her life. Suddenly she knew how her mother had felt when her daughter and granddaughters had left Horcasitas.

On the morning of the sixth the girls helped their mother move her few things from the nunnery to the new house. They would stay with Gertrudis and her family for a few days before the colonists left. It had taken some persuasion to get Eustaquía to agree; she wanted to stay with her "new *papá*."

Paula and two of her friends helped Feliciana dress. They brushed her long hair until it shone, and then helped her pin it high on her head. They fastened flowers and ribbons among the curls and stood back to admire their work.

"You look so beautiful, *Señora*," they said over and over, as Feliciana blushed. "*Señor* López is most fortunate to have such a bride."

When the bells rang, eveyone went into the chapel where *Padres* Paterna and Garcés waited. Feliciana and Juan walked in last, with Tomasa and Eustaquía on each side. The chapel was a bower of flowers and greenery, testimony to the love and devotion the Indian girls had for the young Spanish "Doña" who was willing to live as they did.

As Feliciana knelt during the service, she felt humbled by the love being showered upon her by all these friends, and for the man kneeling beside her. The unexpected arrival of *Padre* Garcés had completed Feliciana's "California miracle."

After the religious ceremony the wedding feast was placed on the long tables outside. *Padre* Paterna offered his prayer: thanks for the help the colonists had given him and a hope those present would soon join *Capitán* Anza and conclude their contract with Viceroy Bucareli. Garcés added a toast to the newlyweds—a wish for happiness and a long and abundant life.

After the dining the musicians warmed up their instruments. Feliciana laughed at Juan when he protested he couldn't dance. Bravely, though, he led his radiant bride into the center and they walked a stately promenade. Then *Señor* Peralta, as a stand-in for the father, claimed a dance with the bride. Juan retired, relieved. There was little dancing among the mission soldiers.

Soon most were dancing and having mixed feelings. There was happiness for today and sorrow that soon their lives would go different ways.

After a short rest while the Indian girls served a fruit punch, someone shouted for Feliciana to dance. As though it had been arranged, Luís Peralta stepped up to lead her to the center and the musicians started the *fandango*.

As the tempo stepped up, young Peralta dropped out and once again Feliciana, filled with unbelievable happiness, danced as she had at Tubac. She flashed a flirtatious smile at Juan as she whirled by. At the end, a proud Juan swept her off her feet and swung her around.

"You are so beautiful and you are mine." Juan's love for her shone for all to see. Feliciana again vowed to make their lives the happiest anyone could wish for.

At last everyone surrounded the young couple to walk them to their new home. As they stood in their doorway listening to the serenading by their friends, Juan spoke softly to Feliciana:

"You were—and are—beautiful, *querida*. California is *our* miracle." He lifted the blue good luck charm, knowing its history, and said, "And this shall be the symbol of that miracle."

To the cheers of the onlookers, he picked up his bride and carried her into their new home.

EPILOGUE

Anza had no crystal ball, nor was there really any power in old Juana's blue stone charm to foretell the miracle California held for Feliciana—nor the impact she would have on the new land. Fortunately, the *padres* at each mission kept records of births, marriages and deaths. These tell us much of Feliciana's story after her marriage.

Feliciana and Juan López lived in their little home several years. Records show that a soldier and his wife worked with the San Gabriel Mission Indians, but no names are given. Perhaps they were Feliciana and Juan.

Old Juana with her blue charm had predicted that Tomasa would be a comfort to her mother. There is no doubt that Tomasa was a help with her mother's new babies until her own marriage to Juan Joseph Sepúlveda about 1785. Tomasa had three little boys before her untimely death in 1798.

Thirteen years after her arrival in San Gabriel, Eustaquía married José Pico, who then lived in San Diego. She too fulfilled old Juana's forecast. Of her eight children, two of the three boys became active in California politics. Pío Pico, the second son, was governor of the San Diego-Santa Barbara section when the north and south tried to separate. During the war between Mexico and the United States Pío and his brother, Andrés, fought with the Californios. Later Andrés became a United States citizen and took an active role in politics. He was elected first as an assemblyman and in 1860 was a state senator.

Three of the Pico girls were named Jacinta, Feliciana and Tomasa, for their grandmothers and two aunts.

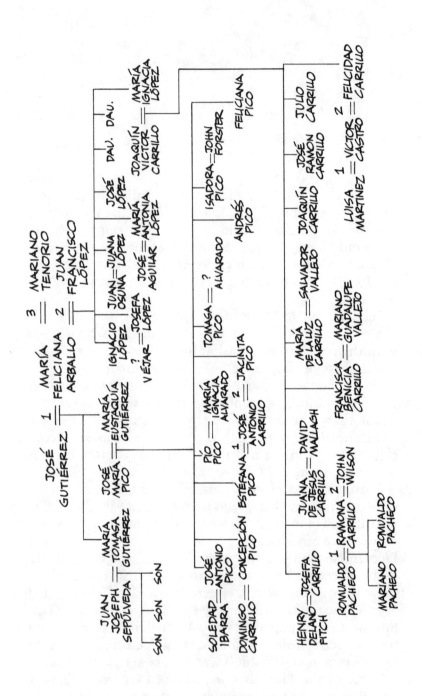

Feliciana's California Family

Feliciana and Juan López had six girls and two boys. Two little girls died before they were six, but the rest grew to adulthood and married. After twenty years of marriage Juan died in 1797, leaving Feliciana again with daughters who were four and six, plus two older ones. Sometime later Feliciana married Mariano Tenorio.

Perhaps Juana's prediction was also for the youngest child of Feliciana and Juan, María Ignacia de la Candelaría. She married Joaquín Victor Carrillo, who came from a powerful southern California family. Joaquín and María lived in San Diego with their brood of twelve children. Their daughters were esteemed throughout California for their beauty, independence and intelligence—qualities inherited from their grandmother, Feliciana.

One daughter, Josefa, defied Governor Echeandía, who wished to marry her, and with the connivance of her half-cousin, Pío Pico, she eloped with Captain Henry Delano Fitch of Boston.

Their second daughter, Ramona, married Romualdo Pacheco in a double ceremony. Together with the other couple they took an extended honeymoon, visiting many missions and large haciendas, where they were feted with parties and gifts. Romualdo was killed in battle, leaving two small sons, one of whom bore his name.

Ramona then married a Scotsman, John Wilson. When California became an American state, her son Romualdo was elected lieutenant governor, and for a time was acting governor of California.

Mariano G. Vallejo, a handsome young *alférez* from Monterey, caught a glimpse of Francisca Benicia Carillo while he was in San Diego on business for the Mexican governor. It was love at first sight, and two years later they were married. After serving as *comandante* at Yerba Buena, he moved his garrison and family to Sonoma, near the Solano Mission. Here they stayed and eventually celebrated their fiftieth wedding anniversary with many of their sixteen children present. (I have already told the fascinating story of General Vallejo and his family in my earlier book, *Vallejo and the Four Flags*.)

Another Carrillo daughter, María de la Luz, married Salvador Vallejo, the brother of Mariano, and they also moved to Sonoma, where the two sisters saw each other daily.

When the husband of María Ignacia Carrillo died, she received a grant of land near the present city of Santa Rosa, California. She moved the rest of her family there to be near her daughters in Sonoma.

It was natural that these early California families, isolated as they were, would intermarry often. In the first volume of *The Beginnings of San Francisco*, Zoeth E. Eldredge gives the names of those in Anza's expedition and in many cases explains what became of them and their descendants.

Feliciana's miracle was a new land, a beloved husband, and many, many talented children and grandchildren. She did indeed make an impact on California.

BIBLIOGRAPHY

Bolton, Herbert E. *Anza's California Expedition.* 2 Vols. Berkeley: University of California Press, 1930.

Bolton, Herbert E. *History of California.* Vols. II, III, IV. Berkeley: University of California Press, 1930.

Caughey, John Walton. *California.* N.Y.: Prentice-Hall, 1940.

Corle, Edwin. *The Gila River.* N.Y.: Rinehart, 1951.

Dawson, Grace. *The Story of Our Southwest Corner.* N.Y.: MacMillan, 1955.

Eldredge, Zoeth S. *The Beginnings of San Francisco.* Vol. 1. S.F.: Zoeth S. Eldredge, 1912.

Hunt, Rockwell D. *California in the Making.* Caldwell: Caxton Printers, 1953.

Lavender, David. *California: A Bicentennial History.* N.Y.: W. W. Norton, 1976.

McKittrick, Myrtle. *Vallejo, Son of California.* Portland: Binfords and Mort, 1944.

Northrop, Marie. *Spanish-Mexican Families: Early California, 1769-1850.* New Orleans: Polyanthos, 1976.

Norton, Henry K. *The Story of California.* Chicago: A. C. McClurg, 1913.

Older, Mrs. Fremont. *Love Stories of Old California.* N.Y.: Coward-McCann, 1940.

Pico, Pío. *Historical Narrative, 1801–1894.* Glendale: Arthur H. Clark, 1973.

Pourade, Richard F. *Anza Conquers the Desert.* San Diego: The Union-Tribune, 1971.

Pourade, Richard F. *The History of San Diego.* Vol. I. San Diego: The Union-Tribune, 1960.

Riley, Frank. *De Anza's Trail Today.* L.A.: World Way Publishing, 1976.

INDEX

accommodations for, 16; leads Alabado, 20; at Tumacácori, 39; conducts mass, 61, 62, 69, 90, 94, 102, 123, 155; illness of, 68-70, 81, 82, 96; among Yumas, 75-78; health improves, 106; insists on staying with Anza, 128, 129, 150, 156
Franciscan Order, 46

Garcés, Padre Francisco, xiii, 23, 46, 61; funeral service at San Xavier del Bac, 51, 54; interprets for Anza and Palma, 73-75; illness of, 78; crosses Colorado and leaves expedition, 80, 82, 87, 91; at San Gabriel, 165-167
Gila River, 61-63, 66-70, 75
Grijalva, Juan Pablo, 88, 92, 149
Gutiérrez, Ignacio, 70
Gutiérrez, José, 3, 5, 8, 9
Gutiérrez, Señora, 70

Hohokam Indians, 63
Horcasitas, 4, 7, 12, 14
Hot Springs, 69, 70

Ignacio Cañon, 27
Indians, xiii, 23, 24, 54, 56, 80-82; Apache, 6, 9, 15, 21, 27, 28-31, 35, 36, 46, 47, 52, 53, 55, 67, 76; Cajuenche, 86, 87; Diegueño, 119; Gabrielino, 120, 124-131, 133-135, 157, 169; Hohokam, 62, 63; Luiseño-Cahuilla, 96-98; Pima, 55, 57-59, 61, 63; Yuma, xiii, 64-66, 68, 69, 72-75, 77, 85, 86, 95
Indian Villages, 57, 72, 76, 85

Jesuit Order, 45-47

Kearny, Stephen W., xiii
Kino, Padre Eusebio Francisco, 45, 46, 53, 62, 63

Laguna de Santa Olaya, 86, 87, 91
Las Lagunas de Hospital, 66, 67
Lewis and Clark, xii
Linares, Gertrudis, 98, 100-104
Linares, Ignacio, 102
Linares, Salvador Ignacio, 101, 102
López, Juan Francisco, 112ff; 169, 171
López, María Ignacia de la Candelaría, 171

Magdalena River, 27
Mexico City, xiii, 17, 37, 76
Missions, xi, xii, 37; San Carlos Borromeo del Carmelo, xii, 122, 150; San Diego de Alcalá, xi, 119, 124, 127, 128, 139, 149, 150; San Francisco Solano, 171; San Gabriel Arcangel, xii, 107, 112, 113, 119-159, 169; San Xavier del Bac, 31, 46, 51-54; Tumacácori, 31, 35, 39, 44-46
Monterey, xii, 122, 150
Moraga, José Joaquín, xi, xii, 50, 51, 54, 75, 88, 92, 93, 124, 139, 141, 148-150, 157-159
Mules, 20, 24, 25, 27, 30
Muleteers, 25, 30, 54, 55, 61, 141, 147-149, 158, 159
Muños, Francisco, xiii, 12ff

THE AUTHOR

Esther Jacoby Comstock was born in San Francisco short-ly before the 1906 earthquake and fire. When the ashes settled, her banker father moved his family across the bay to Oakland, where she grew up. She attended the University of California at Berkeley for two years before transferring to the College of the Pacific in Stockton. In 1926 she received her B.A. and teaching credential, and married architect Floyd B. Comstock. Not until her third (and youngest) child was attending the same college did she finally pursue a teaching career.

For ten years she taught primary grades, and then continued for five years as a substitute teacher, mostly in the fourth grade. From this experience came her desire to improve the quality of California history books available to young people. Her first book, *Vallejo and the Four Flags*, was published by Comstock Bonanza Press in 1979. It is the life story of General Mariano Vallejo and is used in hundreds of California and Nevada schools as a supplementary text in the study of California history; moreover, it has been read by hundreds of adults and children for sheer pleasure. After living in Contra Costa County for many years, the Comstocks now reside in Stockton, California.

Designed and produced by Dave Comstock.
Text type is Trump Mediæval, Initials and
Display type are Augustea Inline, composed by
Comstock Bonanza Press and Dwan Typography.
Printed on Booktext Natural Hi Bulk, Basis 55,
by BookCrafters, Inc.
Library edition bound in Holliston Roxite
Amerspun Buckram 70143.